Sonar

Sonar

By Kristian Enright

TURNSTONE PRESS

Turnstone Press
Artspace Building
206-100 Arthur Street
Winnipeg, MB
R3B 1H3 Canada
www.TurnstonePress.com

Turnstone Press gratefully acknowledges the assistance of the Canada Council
for the Arts, the Manitoba Arts Council, the Government of Canada through the
Canada Book Fund, and the Province of Manitoba through the Book Publishing
Tax Credit and the Book Publisher Marketing Assistance Program.

Printed and bound in Canada by Friesens for Turnstone Press.

Library and Archives Canada Cataloguing in Publication

Enright, Kristian, 1980-
    Sonar / Kristian Enright.

ISBN 978-0-88801-391-0

    I. Title.

PS8609.N72S66 2012   C811'.6   C2012-904937-9

for my parents,
Eva Fritsch and Robert Enright

as well as professors Dennis Cooley and David Arnason

Sonar

A Narrative Fragment: A/ The "Character" via the "Narrator" Colin Verbanofsky Makes an Entrance

A man rushed through the doors of the hard school of life without a knock. The Health Sciences Centre's mechanical doors parted to welcome him, brimming with near cyborg enthusiasm, in the polluted night and his trails of tissued ghost. A few moments later his initial identity seemed forgotten as he sat with opiate calm in the limbo of the hospital lobby. He then requested, with a suitably strange gesture, bureaucratic papers. They would act as a kind of "worded teddy bear," he stated, smiling vaguely. "I am feeling emotions too complex for a time of instant gratification," he added, in his already considerable history of enigmatic non sequiturs.

Frame Break: Organizing His Thoughts

Depression's azure being/ a great waste of energy, displaced and diffused/ where only bug-eyed paranoia/ is watching/ I decided to catch my breath/ for too much change has occurred/ like a cartoon background/ with a sketchy feel by Van Gogh/ as all that I truly register is a sense/ of the inchoate. Breath diffuse blue/ an environmental crisis says emphatically green/ the city moves like physics-defying avalanches outside./ This first night so difficult/ a nurse with a face she barely/ showed (innocence's probably)/ led me to the bed/ why was I already lost/ fooled by the bleached bed sheets/ yellow blankets/ the existence of grey nothing out the window/ and I sat there then a beggar/ sad antennae drooping/ in the next moment with reference to/ a disappearing muse/ confronted with a hospital/ a lighthouse in an antediluvian age/ to this milky marble marvel lost/ the failed parade of white hallways/ the youthful sculpture/ hoping a thinker will use him/ in some symposium everyone will be talking about./ A David standing in relativity/ and nurses silently come and

go/ soon to sleep and dream/ of more than sculptured anatomy.
"So what's the new guy's story?" *A half interested posit of faded whim.*

I did not know then that suicide watch was/ standard procedure/… sets of eyes that seemed like owls/ though the idea seems/ slightly morbid/ to privacy it would be/ magnified a million times in morbidity/ to ignore the conceptual guests./ This is the closest thing/ you have to a saint/ a saint Christopher to go to the brown washroom/ a saint energy to give animation to the nurse… unlike everyone I was avoiding/ a vision with some new colour/ or the focused vision a frame/ that won't allow an image in/ or my healing "vision" only/ I clutched my papers I had wrapped like a scroll.

"Used to work at a frame shop. He was noted as mostly friendless. The closest mention to even an associate was his claiming he might have been framed. That he had been set up or surrounded to put him in ruins. The doctors almost had concussions from scratching their heads." *A disconcerted reporter, spoken perversely.*

The exemplary dream occurred/ that first night/ conceived of my death by eraser/ but I knew that if I lucid dreamed that night,/ I might be able to completely erase/ the image of killing myself/ and thus was able to rest/ almost quietly on the white sheets/ that had I been selfish regarding/ would have been a certain colour flags/ a failed composure *should* I have delta-ed my veins/ or digested the lunar/ pills of pulling puke. I would erase my wrists/ or all parts of me that could hurt anyone./ Then it came/ deep in the sonorous dream/ I wrote a rough version down when I awoke./ I lie on a medical bed/ tied down, and a doctor approaches,/ he has a strange mug/ a guilty plastic surgeon/ but I think he has a pen and eraser/ and he goes to work/ I don't know what I have/ in this situation, disease-wise/ if this isn't some kind of/ totally improvised placebo/ he might amuse his colleagues with./ As I note he is constantly speaking/ of witty things, that is; *being brief*/ and his words not making contact with anything/ an Oscar Wilde who/ would just invent metaphors/ for light in a dark age morality play/ and there would be foolish laughter/ I imagine deeper that this/ Doctor's dinner plate is assisted by/ a shovel and a military collection/ lots of dessert forks and that he has/ a butler for his teeth/ and I think of recommending/ a spokesperson for his yawning.

For some reason I know/ there are bats in my body/ they symbolize the upside-down/ or the right side up/ (if you are the lone kid in the periphery/ outside common interest in the school room/ before the art lecture on Van Gogh begins/.) The Doctor, with deft pencil, erases most/ of my interior, so that the dream/ begins to fade itself, and he touches my brain, prodding/ then: retracts. I was able to lean back/ as if I were swimming/ and was able to float/ for a while. Smile infected/ by Hollywood, he retracts/ fully and finally, and I seem ready/ to wake. But the single detail/ the eraser is gone/ must have snapped off inside me./ I think of a womb in a moment/ that faltered comprehension,/ but I don't know if I do this because/ it is an image of comfort/ or if I think I will have a kind/ of hollowing cancer so/ the flesh melts into events/ a private failure magnified/ a million times by loss./ My first thought when writing was/ I was Rip Van Winkle and I had signed/ a thousand contracts at every degree/ and plateau of dream./ Then came glaring/ like a freakishly muscled messenger/ whose brain in singular acts of will/ had turned light into a dog/ getting the paper, and whose body/ will twitch upon death/ in the finality of a last/ note of an apocalyptic symphony./ Inside of me was a condensed absence/ that perhaps my blue veins had seized excitedly,/ and it becomes an organ/ as complex as the brain is;/ even now I am hesitant to use it in memory/ a heart in hiding.

"He was apparently a closet intellectual," *a rough masculine voice gruffed drolly.*

Can hypochondria become totally internal? I had an interior that had become like the Roman empire, but of endless corners that opened into mirrors and the conqueror is somehow going through

the motions. Why does this emptiness keep getting bigger? Is the eraser somehow alive in a way I can understand? *A spit aqueduct or a spine that just sends nervous energy out. Or an interior for the object to surrender to space...?* For some reason when I woke I composed a diagnosis for this endless expansion: "The Roman Rash."
"I made his bed, I would say he is a dreamer," *a voice said with a thoughtful air.*

I have no relation to light as the dramatic life of hiding makes your drapes a horrible state, an antithesis to a puberty of the emotions. Then a nurse entered and I bit my tongue as if to not show painted red.

Journal of Colin #1

Portrait of the room: obsessive minimalism. On the wall, in small graffiti cursive, something written on a torn flap of wall, the first thing I noted. The room is painfully simple, impelling me to *listen*, all I feel I can do here now. This room is now closed. Hearing a door opening, I could hear the faintest energy of adjectival babble, so very close.

Colin's Frame Break as Sensed by an Elderly Nurse, Vella

"Would the novice sense *it*? Kerouac's mystical pronoun?"
She wondered bright and warmly.
The bed recomposed in silence/ besides a witty
epigraph that she whispered
"pain gives such distracting toys to the emotions
for it to erode till you get to its empty core, like a lollipop
that explodes without taste."
She made a wave pulse with the bed sheets:
  shmoomph smoommph

A sudden soft ripple rise and fall, like dressing space
up, she, well aware of the nightmare's habit
knew it to wear blinds down an alley without a street, with
vagueness astir in the eyes,

Made her watch the sheets fall again and
thought it could momentarily be a water bed
the way a hummingbird in flight is just barely bird

The nurse's smile too subtle for a lighthouse
knowing some spotlights of abstraction here and there,
but she stood up just like that edifice and we might say
metaphysically, she walked away

The room lucidly starched, her shoes
made sounds like inconsequential stones that you could
crash against walls without damage,
anyway into waters gone by.
She was one who could defamiliarize a window
and that is where he would be: looking out
"Any way,"
she said, quick as an excuse.

(It was a quote that meant ubiquity; she could see any way.
Her wise head rose over the rabble
like a cartoon bubble on how to draw better cartoon bubbles.)

Bureaucracy Poem
Found in room by Nurse Vella.

Recent negative emotions have made contact
with the infrastructure, due to the relegation of priorities which need
be inserted and applied to the prudent demeanour of our outreach
    systems
in the broader community. The priorities include that

Sadness is simply bad morale; hence it need be
imposed only as a means of exposing a bad example—
hence it can be exploited for pure manipulative agendas.

As for happiness, (recognized by the board as possible
propaganda) it can be used by our public-spokes-personality
to indicate that "none of your business"
is going well and no external impositions which decrease
productivity levels isolated and not appropriated
by the voices of those who lack efficiency, are unmet: *Sad* does not
have to lead to
the *rampant ornate ness* of melancholy or *emotional disorganization.*
Those who feel too much would, with empty reality, provoke
the use of lofty air conditioning to avoid the downward trajectory of
aforementioned priorities. The use of lofty air is insufficient as a paper
                weight
to the turning of pages of the end of week vacation gone too quickly.
A common balanced air is needed, and slowly sadness
passes through the system; watched with calm, by security
camera omniscience, it walks out below from the office
tower with a *brief case,* the lightest of baggage to a company
of more freedom.
Brief case, this won't take long, he said/ thought with a commercials'
    confidence.

(The Collapse of Order and the Failure of Music)
Ruin of an Impossible Sonnet Taken from Home
of Patient Verbanofsky

T he first thing about the frame is get it
H ung the right way; it is to chaos what
E vil's fall was to the endless pi   t
S howing depths I had never
O
N
N
E
T
S
H
A
P
Ended on a particularly bad no   t.

Abstract Expressionist Wall

"The frame is a kind of border, it is the drawing out of the wall which
art gallery space has 'conquered' in its own neutralizing way. The
idea of the wall being a kind of thing that in history has often existed
to keep out, in a gallery its dimension is often forgotten. In the
imagination a wall prevents exploration, so that it restricts. Unlike
Berlin's, the gallery's wants to say its wall is "just a wall" and its effect
has been to not challenge the work of art. But in reality the wall
protrudes. It hence reverses from the painting model it draws from.
In this institution the wall *absorbs?*"

Slow Sonar

1. Evidence that I am in a monastery...
A young girl, (wearing a **hood** punctuates the white silence) as she darts in this radar dead-zone like the saint of a pinball machine. Here the question "where is coherence?" is felt by everyone?

2. Evidence that I am part of an architectural experiment...
A nurse by the door of a patient with the face of a gargoyle, marble smile; a polite falsity, ears calculating computer chips. Corners here that suggest a waiting room is no longer an official part of this alley of an arcade, they beckon my defection from formal spaces.

3. Evidence that I am in a tomb...
Catatonia is worsened here sloth pried at the walls once but now slowness seems conquering... a romanticist wind rubbing rust? The wind of vagueness would pick a cartoon bubble away so you start wishing for your words to be on **stone**.

4. Evidence that I am at the edge of the world...
A horrible sense of nothing beyond the glass enclosure. A "man maid," Cliff, name discreetly on his chest, walks by... Wittgenstein somewhere in a trench of silence. "The limits of language are the limits of my world," he said. Fluency, ubiquity, molecular, wit, colonial, bird. Do you see it? There is a whole world here. In 1492 Columbus set loose the eventual post-colonial view. Do you see a full world here, from its edge? You need sharp connections. How did I get here?

5. Evidence that I am in a giant closet...
Why do I think that a straight jacket is no self-loving corset? Or is it a floatation jacket?

Sadness: emphatically not happiness, no crayon for your
colouring book.
The black outlines form the streets you should not cross
without envisioning. The colours beginning to leak out,
water colour, helpless landscape.

Melancholia: hoping your sadness can be better than before
with such eloquent naming and connotations more exiting than
chemical lingo. An actual muse lingers over you, faint
by lack of belief—
How you might describe depression to your child during their puberty.

Depression: straight from medical texts for you.
It is flatness, the de-winged crushed in a textbook
falling without moving; a figurative trap
where imagination bleeds to death without even psychedelics.

Misery: a universal term that stretches a relative journey
across these other terms without distinction.
The memory of happiness is essential to these roles;
in the first, happiness fades between a simple pole of happy and sad.
In the second it is distance and time and the dream of a meaningful
ornament that makes you useless as art.
In depression is it pure exaggeration and unmixed
misery and happiness are a wrestling match and
if you are in a sadness no one has yet here
mentioned, you might well want happiness to lose
so that misery will no longer be ashamed
standing on its own terms. The idea of a monument of parody written
of voices in stone, silent technically, is, however, how confused
and paradoxical one can feel while here.
**But try saying something that people want to preserve the wall
    "said" boldly**

The patient, Colin Verbanofsky, has been admitted for what appears to be severe depression tempered by/with considerable mania, likely bi-polar. During mania the patient sees some things as if they were doubled, as if antecedents were mutating, leading to incomprehensible babble. His sleeping has been considerably varied, at one point waking up several times and at other times not wanting to get out of bed. He claimed our *ink blot* readings are subject to a thing he calls "new criticism": "they are ink blots," he told us emphatically. "You do not have an outside authority on their meaning." We would like to refer this patient to Doctor Earwinker, who has expertise in the intersecting of psychology and art.

First Group Meeting with Other Patients
Based on First Impressions Recorded in a New Notebook:
Art of First Impression/isms

1.

Her face was an oval realization of cream with huge owl eyes of
insomnia and a cooing sound. Jenna is actually her name, and her
smile was a distraction. Her voice was like someone confessing to
a priest, merely admitting emotions, as she dyed her milk face with
rose tea, but I could tell she was ashamed of her illness. But she
mentioned a "reflective surface" in a philosophic way. That was how
she saw the world, which would undulate.

2. And,

The next person was a man who stated, "I am the only voice that
matters. All others are derivative of mine. The world is my welcome
mat and *you* are *all* the syn*tax* to my Caesar." His voice was rigid:
yet he puns—the lowest form of humour—(from his alleged heights)
but I thought, "he listens to his inner jester." His name is Jack Deride
and his grandeur was so obvious it was like being in a great building
whose architect is standing by you as you enter for the first time and
every detail was a reflection of him.

3. And,

"Pure nervous energy," introduced himself as raised by hippies,
that his name was "raindrop" and wanted his last name to be
"evaporation." His name was Rick Genevive, he said, "just call me
that." His wit was evident, his mysteriousness almost cheapened but
preserved by an effusive charm, dangling like a wit's stop watch on
go. He also possessed energy like a cornucopia: "a careening vessel of
spirited energy is the licence plate in my head." He has ego boundary
"issues," he explained. Could he want to be a martyr for parody? I
wondered. He had the kind delivery of a stand-up comedian.

4. And,

The voice that emerged next was haunting and you wondered at her paranoid metaphysics when she muttered, "I made a Eucharist of crust while sermonizing in the orphanage." Where did she come from? An antecedent to my confusion? When asked to say something about herself she said only: "in an imagination factory how do you transcend the factory, besides through fact?" Her name is Allison Ventrenko. She was the first person I felt a considerable affectionate emotion towards in a long time.

5. And,

The next patient, Roary Lionessa, seemed not to be reading for us, acted as if we just happened to be in the room. But she stated that although this is not a house, it is an institution which has the pleasant synonym "home" and she spoke of indignation at being forced into a nutshell. Her voice was rich with rhetoric and slang. "An individual against the whole of creation," as Ginsberg had said of Bob Dylan. She read from a prepared statement, which I later attained, speaking monotone as if bored with the language. "There is an angel in the house/ tale of cat and mouse..." The speech lasted long enough to be a manifesto for an important moment.

6. And,

The next person, blasted by sleep, whenever he spoke, seemed to represent, though not admit, impediments. He would be revealed as stopping thinking for reasons of perhaps futility; but the tragedy is that he is surprisingly thoughtful and this is what makes him "useless." Vorseth Baltigore is his name. "I know—am already aware—that my name sounds like a medieval war instrument, but I barely even fight the abstract fight anymore. I am a Beckett by-product." When he said he loved long zombie walks, I thought that had I not heard him speak, I might have assumed him catatonic.

7. And,

The face I looked at was clearly tormented but mostly angry. His name is Milton Phoenix and his eyes looked as if he had been reading *Paradise Lost* all night to distract himself from some other, realer, terrible thoughts. Thinks he is a prophet. That was apparent. I wondered if he thought in a religious sense or an artistic one. His voice mingled the imperative with the subjunctive. He has a kind of "schizophrenia or split personality," he said. "And I know dark," he added. "Most people sit in the theatre when the projector isn't on and call *that* dark."

8. And,

Too friendly to ever be mysterious, once he spoke he was almost laconic, but said we should call him Sal. He was evidently quiet but there was a kind of glow to him, as if his skin was singing. He had a kind of strange confidence, as if from another source other, and more purely than, his presumably tiny ego. I noted that as he spoke, he seemed to be reacting to something at a perfect distance; not too far as to be some distant ideal, but not so close as to reward instant gratification.

9. And,

The final person I met was constantly hitting her arm, with considerable focus and rigour. She claimed she was trying to cause a new artery of some kind. "A bruise artery?" I almost asked, incredulous. Then I remembered with some horror my eraser dream and felt suddenly self-conscious. Her name was Betty, she said, looking up, and then resumed her actions while adding nonchalantly: "There is something very wrong—or right—inside my head. It likes to talk but not listen." I considered that this was likely about schizophrenia, in a simple and pithy way.

After First Group: Staccato Poetry of a Once Emotional Untouchable

Confessional poetry after therapy

One hurried prelude to a fairy tale afternoon while
pondering: a glass of wine,
New Yorker cartoons, and old testament laughter,
a leper came to my apartment gates…
Later, my liminal blink
snipped a perfectly formed tear.
It was a personalized atom bomb
causing a seismic shudder.

I realized I had nothing inside of me desiring to reach out:
my charity a sterilized glove, waving at drowning.
There was only a maniacal cackle,
a force field forced by tragic slap stick awareness,
play-by-play deconstructions of the world.

But when this leper appeared at the gate I was just
a typical octopus intestine'd corset pen-prick.
This figure said I was ill
but no more so than the world
around me, and then said I was loved
by the unformed, and left me.

Later, in the dead glow of a television
in the hospital TV room where the teasing apparition
rapped its rays around me, a cheap catharsis
from a late night show occurred and I had an x-ray epiphany
of myself and I realized I was a Blakean cartoon.
(Imagist poem awareness of the skeleton even when writing about *life.*)

My eye did not extend to the streets, intimate below.
My hand had thus pressed fast forward on a stunned reality, impatient.
My taste was for pleasure: teeth a picket fence before a wall.
My cologne defamiliarized mist over everyone's possible dead body.
My ear heard music when I spoke but otherwise seemed clogged.

So, with all my soul, I went to the bathroom and
vomited as if I was engaged in self-expression.

As if from a black hole a phantom arm reached out and
caressed my face/ was the glow of Keats in the
warm bed by flashlight/ (as if by tears my eyes were formed).

I wanted to tell Blake psychosis has a human brain,
and an inhuman melting face applied to self.
And health has the symmetry of a thought train
between a monk's and philistine's wealth?

It is only now that I think of loving myself
as an image: a delta leaving my hand
becomes deformed as if to become new
and yet remains a hand   that holds multiple epiphanies
to sustain it yet the delta seemed skeletal until the water's touch…

A Sleuth is Reborn: A Starting Point

Seated in cold aloneness, in a gaping confession of a book I read:
"All my literature has been an imitation of a literary cackle in my head."
Why does this strike such a sloppy but powerful chord?
The heart-strings and the horn sections gored.
And then, as I listened, I heard a precise utterance,
whispered, so faint I barely caught it: a voice, clear,
distinct, but not on the fence...
"Can *you* represent *me*?"
but it was no matter for it became ever stranger,
with startling light. (A pronoun of light becomes a swift
iconic parade, a friend, Chris, said later). Then, it repeated:
"Can you represent me?" without emphasis, perhaps with
       personification fading?
Several minutes of confusion resulted; with wit, I took from
       Shakespeare,
"giv[ing] myself pause" in an anxiety of un-fluence.
I decided to take it as a general challenge. Imagine all I possessed was
a piece of paper and only that question, an endless segue.
Yet this statement
seemed to have existed before this moment.
As an image of seeing double I imagined this question
on a tombstone
as if I were Sherlock Holmes.

Initial Voice of Health: Plain Hallucinatory Language
Voice, a suspicious pleasant easy-going tone, polished and assuring:

"It might seem strange to start anything with 'happily ever after'
but we do. We learn this phrase early on in life. As we get older
we discover the same phrase applied to thoughts of the after-life,
knowing we live between. For that reason, we consulted people
dealing with depression, who decided to defeat 'a life interrupted'
with Prozac, which is now available for children, in all colours,
including blue, the former official colour for depression. Science
(no longer represented by a faceless levitating lab coat), reminds us
that we are safe. The big bad wolf is not able to speak his mind: 'The
better to de-personify you with,' it would say if it could. Could you
not imagine Hansel and Gretel dropping pills to find their way out
of the forest? There they would be, standing in a farmer's harvesting
field. Science, which brought you the microscope and telescope,
suggests the simple moral of the story: we are not out of the woods
until we have consumed science's symbols—Prozac... *The voice
subliminal/ sycophantic, concentrated around a single image.* Nor are
we crude hunters in primordial dark *(Prozac brand appears brightly
against dark background, price ranges marked).* But we are the organs
which hold up our home and prepare our children for the future
(voice here that would be used to speak to a child didactically)... The
brain is quickly replacing the heart as the only place to live. You will
be happy, ever after, after you have tried *Prozac.* Call this number on
your screen and get your complimentary package: happiness should
not be difficult, should it?—we at Prozac understand that."

On the screen: The image of a man and a woman on a beach
together, very openly happy, and no one else is on the beach, no
impediments what-so-ever that could distract them. Perhaps this
suggests that we adults can believe—for a single instance—in the
vision of happiness in a fairy tale. But then we would look up, ahead
at the beach, and realize the couple are far from their cottage and that
means they will have to walk a great distance and no one, in their

reality, has a camera or a memory for the condensed realization. If it has the unity of "happily ever after..." The voice of science is linked to healthy images; is health reflected in language, a prudent set of words, like the archaeologist in the antique store?

Sequence: The Great Trap
The window replaces television, "otherwise a hole in the argument of a secluded genius."

1.
The actors of reality are too slick for me...quadruple signifiers.
To defect from "this box place" leads to chaos and falling into
non-description: garish adjectives. Or,
carpe diem in a ceiling crack: is that why do I not feel containable
in this tiny room and yet, desire its containment?

Domesticated lives/ charitable images of health/ actors
walking their dogs in un-foggy certainty.
The air is fresh but not "defamiliarized."
With fleeting heroics they pick up shit like
one of the Last MetaNarrative Heroes, that of community.
                    I am watching
distant towers, spent messengers and epitaphs of abbreviations.
I am beginning to learn that the normal
world is a referential reservoir. A normal day is a
general map, in isolation. Not what I had thought,
when historical time oppresses and
we make hasty speeches on grocery lists.

But how do these sane–other people move so easily?
Despite superhighways mocking me/ everywhere: deadends of life.

When I was a framer I could imagine how
people would die according to their habits, a
puzzle game of graves. Now nothing fits.
There are no proper shapes, just smoke untangling.
The graves of bureaucrats go to geology
bureaucracy where time will shuffle them in a mountain's strata:
a romanticist on top is trying to capture the wind
like an ambitious paperweight. But,
reality imprisons me, questioning it or not.
I try to cram my intestines into the brain hole…
                        Now that I am
Here I am dealing with a labyrinth puzzle
from there, a glorified trap? Am I then just a prisoner
dreaming better distractions?

2.
When you give up the labyrinth is strangely immanent
so when you keep moving you learn;
the air conditioning's a coiling of cool snakes of air
is a lonely Minotaur's phallus for all I know.

This trap does not look like one, despite the halls of this space
that made me think of an experiment. A dog on a leash
pulls all watchers along a beautiful area
where Agoraphobia and Claustrophobia are neighbours.

But is the trap in words? You will not be conquered
by political correctness there
is no place that wants to keep you so when I say it is a trap,
you see why I invoke a labyrinth, to make it a place.

3.
The stigma of being here; the *fact of these walls*
having the text on them bewilders me. I recall the straight jacket,
"no self-loving corset," but I sit in perfect calm not needing it.
A Da Vinci drawing that invents a light switch
ending the Dark Ages and my will stands before it
delirious with wonder but I am distant from simple answers.
"The writing is on/ off the wall," a voice says.
The language is too able to speak of
an obscure perception that feels a lot like a
system (labyrinth evidence) and you just discovered it.
You see how I mantra the word "system" in possible
deconstructive chaos
as with the idea of a labyrinth instead of a trap.
'Tis folly to be funny
when humans toil for something
to console them *like Alka-Seltzer marble in acid*
rain simulated in a glass of exact measurements.

This is my realism; going where? A devil statistic? Society
regards me as a lost stone, a "worse than senseless thing"
and a pill suddenly recalls Einstein, its mass equals energy.
I see that I am a great director who is given just a normal day
until the cloud system of mania
with a sunny day's baggage of lightning comes and all
is out of proportion; you can see it in my language, can you not?
Something has to happen to my language, but what?
It clings to margins like spines.
Emotions scanned through a microscope/ up against the wall.

The nurse said: "You are always on your path no matter what. Whether throwing garbage out in an alley, or working for a mediocre despot." She laughed. "Even in a maze, you are on your path, don't you see? Or when you are trapped, then too." She smiled like a lighthouse.

Mantra Dance: A Human behind the Institution

"You are   always

         on   your

              path"   (no
                              Matter)
    what

or
         how   the
                                              scene
                   is

constructed: trees of epiphanies
          knees in mud; natural ritual
               or
     how fast everything   goes by

                    or a clock struck with paralysis
          a penguin
               rather than a cuckoo
to show how time emphatically doesn't   always   fly

here sometimes
                              pokes   out

              when there is a space/ time
continue 'em
          conceiving of an attention
                                              span
                                                   of
              wings

but why do we   take lessons   of linearity

from poets who are clearly
                                dancing
                with the crooked line, physicists of the lover's shadow

                And no one's   lines are only
        their   own
                so   maybe
        a
road is a place   after all
        in a grander scheme of things   you are always on your path
(repeat).

The sidewalk awaits with tepid sunshine
with children's hand imprints from when the
concrete was wet like the last one
Kerouac could stand in mythic perfection to: youth making
                                an impression on him.
                                        Then   a
                                                foot
                                        print   too,

                Amazingly   my old self

        left

Rick: Overheard/ Under Hints

It is what the brain *imagines* of the body
that is the case. The zombie is beyond the consumer
image, without polish (and coordination).
But they want enlightenment to be tangible, don't you see?
Everyone can relate to that… in a way the zombie would
make illness of the body there, in the brain, to alleviate it from thought.
The script for the zombie could be *cue cards from a note book* and
the zombie is the true everyman!

   The idea of what mind over brain could signify excited me as a
vision so much that I went to tell Nurse Vella about it (parenthesis
explains the nonsensical.): "I saw them carry away a fat mask! (of
gluttony, a consumer above) with my lost… and found mind—even
here—at the sanctified place of mere appearance! (in the asylum
where you don't see the illness beyond a glazed eye, just behaviour).
The mind is not just a jelly fish! (a gooey object as with a tongue-
whetted candy). A jelly fish in ink there must be more than a garbage
dump in the mind. But the zombie brain, the zombie brain waits at
the sacrificial altar to achieve mind.

A River of Logic Melting in the Mind and Heart

   I am trying to figure out who I was or what I was and why I felt
there is a stream of consciousness/ sewer below all being blurs/
and our names for things as arrogant and Godlike even if I think
of a nice stream in Victorian literature in a progressive tense,
progressing always; but not in all ways *progressive* (so keeps itself).
But really there is a sewer of consciousness, a river once was there
but stagnation is so great that I move my thoughts and I see changing
feelings as if something expressionist upon drunkenness altered

perception, things blurred and unformed. What I felt found its own form and I felt like leaving. Am becoming very suspicious of my thoughts; I don't trust them. Am I a pathological liar in a house of mirrors who lost his path and his logic? I feel that I was like a frozen river and now my syntax can be like fragments of ice as a movement to a Doctor's raised eyebrow commences. A somehow non-intelligent geek (= mystic!) *with just a single aforementioned clue or representation?*

So when I write, I have to take my time; this allows me to make sense.

1. A colossal rudder grazes through mollas'd moneyed numerals... money signs get disfigured.

2. Can only speak when depressed at times; "what you feel will find its own form."

3. The following principle was added by the character/author, and not anachronistically;
   Poly-phoney; I feel my (unique) literary voice is "phoney." This word is like "difference" in deconstruction. However, sometimes I cannot tell whether in my mind I have written something or heard it, lending the term to my whole voice.

Vision of Sadness: "Suffering is One Very Long Moment"

My old friend Christopher, the rainy-day alchemist and I, semi-pilgrims, walked around the neighbourhoods near the hospital. For people today, we have a great vision of sadness, and it is represented in the feeling of Jack Kerouac's writing. He was ambient, like the incense of a burn-out, could see shapes of smoke as if a new world had been placed in the air, but a swift birth as he flowed along the road like a magpie of dying hearts. Here was a man who could look at a beautiful old house and conceive of the sad bowing trees sacrificed to make it, and he would say there were ghosts who came back to do menial work for a desolate family still living there. You can tell because of the way the old lady sweeps when night's curtain is up, she blows the dust back down as she sweeps so that it does not look ghostly. He was so aware of the futility of things that had it not been for his speed of writing, had he slowed down, all human suffering would have been imprinted on his mind and gained weight there. Once you read him, this all becomes very apparent.

Chris said ,"We should be physicists of feeling... you sense it, don't you? Even the world of surfaces is crying out; the paratactic is painful here. Good thing they made light faster than dark; it is precisely because of the connections you make in sadness that makes it slow. 'Suffering is one very long moment,' said Oscar Wilde explaining, implicitly, wit; its speed is just like happiness." That's what Chris said, and he tossed a stone across some puddles in our local wasteland. "Think of it right now, amid all this useful exemplary ugliness. Sadness all at once would be a form of trauma, a train wreck in Nirvana, like Boethius looking at God separate from time. Does darkness play connect-the-stars geologically?" Chris was also known as the "Heaven-Headed Hell-O Centrist."

Attitude Towards a Grey Day in Winnipeg:
The Upside-Down-ness of Depression

"Shy world underneath hides in modest colours, as if censorship were
diffused by a politically correct second- or third-rate cause and both die
interrupting each other, and were buried there."

The skies; diffusing smoke, an exiled ghost
vomiting the stomach it no longer possesses.
Winnipeg; city of hotels for lamed explorers...
Captain Hook gone eunuch in one of our rain-clogged
potholes... gratuitous wind falsely exorcising
itself in a strip show of all things. Yet
if Winnipeg were a flag, it would be holding on
to the North Pole. There is a parable of a gate
the way the thought of leprosy is detectable
when a child puts on rounded mittens, the way
the fingers you put a finger on, have such cold connections.

The grey, as if the first exterior designers said
"This latest translation of grey matter can't exactly
cover that sky, so maybe grey goes with grey.
Concrete is in vogue." Luckily, the pillars of our
civilization involve a tree house, found
somewhere in Wolseley amid the squirrels
and Henry David Thoreau who there could have
impersonated the life of J.D. Salinger.
Depression:
A child with a big room and toys that seem neutral through dullness.
The small spreading feeling makes you feel
"microcosmic" but there is a little existential
document you can sign on a napkin blown to you.

A puppy dog's energy is impossible, an ideal with severed mind
the grey day is the limbo of memory, the stuffing
that is missing is the grey smoke
vanishing like the souls in Hades, the stuff
memory is made of must not possess any of this strange pollution.
But sadness is tragic big here; to not feel it would be a tragic flaw.
To make it your own prevents you from being tragic of it.
Winnipeg was made by performative Gods
who said, stumbling, "anybody who knows no
Euclid can go to confusion corner and see what you
would name it." Epiphany of space:
Einstein's light speed on the prairie: non-movement
except emigration. Winnipeg is afflicted
with Dublin-esque paralysis, except for the
wave of suburbia that is the city escaping.

The skies are a congregation of old bruises buried in a grey sky, there is
no single road. All roads try to leave, but buildings impede, tempting
you to drown in the sky which here floods. Which also is a great sponge
lets loose our sweat upon us.

Two Non Sequiturs of Reality

1. Ivory Tower Insulation: Nurse Vella
"The walls do indeed at times have eyes and ears but they
have no bothersome touch: perfectly smooth—feel'um!
Like sliding out of silk bed sheets!
Note no revolving doors, you usually come and stay awhile
lose your dizziness from the outside world. You can almost feel
intimacy but were it made to seem too much a home
you wouldn't want to ever leave! Oh, and a 'Freudian' couch here?
That's an easy chair that can *downright* lie.
We are modern here, a couch is just a couch!
You also shouldn't think of the halls as a rat maze.
Some people with a whole *wallup* of cynicism think *that* way."

2. Notebook
"It is better to scream how? at existence than why?
Howwwwlll! A voice said in a way that reminded me of a poem.
Best minds, generating? I saw (with my mind's eye)
something that was missing: (your voice here)."
How do I scream and represent the fading hints I see of other things?

For Their New School of Life: An Old/ New Argument

"—What did they teach in school? That we should all be
individuals, at least to pass rhetoric class. To be inside at night
and the whole world locked up and tightened. Borders. Borders
everywhere: what the fuck? No, now is the time— we need to update
the *flâneur*. The *flâneur* being available for people of "no class" and
escape from institutions and experience a world that is not ours yet,
but will be. Should we not also be exposed to the reality of a coffee
shop on an early Tuesday afternoon like verisimilitude, say, in art,
as a wise teenager would posit? In the nuthouse we need master the
nutcracker. *It is like learning Euclid's geometry/ and then being told, as
by an authoritative voice/ that, no, you cannot be an astronaut/ and go
off into space…* I'll give you that line," she said, nudging me. Having
escaped, we went to Confusion Corner where we considered Euclid's
five laws and also *Seed Catalogue*. "This road is the shortest distance
between nowhere and nowhere." The words seemed to strike us as
ironically universal considering our city's nowhere-ness and that
nowhere can be anywhere.

Song Under the Bridge/ Example of Escape/ Outside
Continuity

The bridge swoops irresponsibly over the graffiti
the spectacle of a day ending and no one is
taking minutes, it seems as though the towers have been
realized and now time is falling
—and no one knows what that means, exactly, yet
picture snow-globes filling with bureaucrat's confetti.
A re-aimed middle finger will give directions
to a utopian vacation; the homeland of instant ruins
                    lies beyond.

The suburbs hold historic visitations with the image of traffic
and yet a particular road is that to
which, under the elevated border, dawn
of the bridge, does register another awareness of time,
a melting clock still telling time, a drip per second
is still order: (concept of time-faith to office people).
The end of the day...
But I feel our fantasy is also foolish, that it will melt forever.
Hence, you might fantasize that the graffiti
if you pass it too quickly is
written on the under but not back side of history.
"It symbolizes irresponsibility if you look," said Jenna,
with a touch of perfect ambiguity.

(Roary spray-painted "writing is deaf"
as an academic out-joke on one of the pillars).
That is when Jack said he wanted to be
renamed "Graffitius Maxim-us."
"What maxims do you propose?"
"That we forge, unapologetic ally, a set of sayings that are
known as "mull appropriatisms."

"My, you are on fire today, Jack," said Rick.

I later wrote this poem about it, the above lines, that is:

The architects of hell are
building slums but the walls
are of highest quality
one of them reaches heaven's misty regions
with false idol wallpaper design
and dreams of lightning—brief chandeliers of God.

Discussion Summary: A Winnipeg River Goes Crystal

We ended up speaking of our "problems," an issue for Rick,
who explained that gregariousness was part of feeling exposed,
something we all related to; we spoke of the analogy of lacking a
skull, *paranoid thought* tantamount to *open bleeding* as if the *brain
were exposed.* Allison explained her crust statement as her personal
(subjective) mention of bricolage and not wasting anything, and that
the orphanage was what she called our hospital. She also said that her
obsessions were cosmically inspired. "The whole world winked her
into confusion, like a magpie wielding a computer chip in the night,"
she said, speaking of herself in the third person, adding, "the whole
world is disposable without ritual." Jack agreed, his huge egg forehead
a dome of consent. In rare candour, he admitted he sometimes felt
if people did not listen to him he would disappear. He said the word
"being" was Allison's ideal word. He seemed as if he were speaking
to the world, as Roary sometimes did. Allison's imagination swelled.
She claimed she was inventing a universe with polyphony and that
her genesis would be "in all languages except 'klingon' because that
would mean some joke of the image of the thing holding onto its
word through its sound." She thought that "things inside themselves

should consider being everything else. That comparison could evoke a child clinging to its mother." I was fascinated, and thought of her even as others spoke. We all then spoke of how the institution was externally normal as a building, and yet we could not describe it internally, and were puzzled as to why. None of us mentioned any technical or medical terms of diagnosis, as our imaginations were the stuff coping was made of.

Roary's Movie Intro: A Complication of Her Skipping Argument

"Into a diner, looking to kill boredom, a couple of just-grown-out-of *Clockwork Orange* goons enter. However, the two heroes in the diner (the ones who now look like anybody) affect the way the camera moves. One looks carefully at the other possible hero and then carefully at the chalkboard eraser, a device lingering near the dinner-special sign. He then looks at the face of the one goon, and then looks at a pencil indicating that he will use it to prove it 'mightier than the sword.' In a flash, both goons are erased and the heroes fulfill their roles, getting chalk in the goon's eyes. This involves using things found in school. *Both of those tragic goons were elementary school drop outs.*" Roary then pointed out that Winnipeg was diagnosable as grandiosely mad because the buildings from boom town anticipation do not correlate with the city in actuality. I recalled the junction called Confusion Corner, and wondered if this somehow proved that reading. I also realized obeying "ego boundaries" could have resulted in the goon's succeeding in Roary's story.

Upon Asking Roary What She Was Thinking in a Coffee Shop
(Assumed Schizophrenic Confession Poem)

"No real name, alienessa alias in an I'm-personal
universe epitapping my fingers on a fake
stone table top, waiting with infinite impatience
for the future to show up. I like the phallic
ambiguity of a corset and a volcano, crossed. I am always thinking
of tomorrow, and the mysterious idea that 'there is a voice
within and without, a voice I am waiting for.'
A kind of blur I would make you could say my preface
gets in your masquerade, I'm *that* in your face."

RETURN to INSTITUTION
Quotes of Mild Evidence of Hidden Meanings

"If I lost my personal bracelets, I would lose my mind with them."
    Zeugma.

"Do I only exist if you say so?" A rhetorical question.

"Time for lock up!" Performative statement, a series of doors close.
    Slam. Slam.

"If you had gotten hurt, we would have been responsible. Do you expect that I could simply *fabricate* an explanation for my superiors? We are keeping you safe here, do you not know that? What do you think this is? Disney Land?"

"Sanity is the ultimate winner, or as we would say now, the ultimate *colonizer*. If we were tornadoes you would say well, we had bad breath, didn't we? You have the last metanarrative. Or perhaps we have it also, but without any empowerment. We had to escape to not be restricted, cliché as it is."

"Much of what you say sounds more than a little grandiose. I hope the size of your room does not offend you." He said this sarcastically with a sense of real disregard. "We are anticipating a very complex diagnosis…. However, it might be entirely reasonable to suggest that to treat the mind as a place of exploration is useful."

"Exploration!? Haven't you heard about myth?! Roland Barthes!? Do you know what I symbolize if I were in a straight jacket—that dinner jacket (also morning, noon and night jacket) you imagine me dressed in? No one would ever think I just don't know how to put on a lab coat. I will try not to take politically correct offence at your conflating of 'colonizer' with 'explorer.' How would you like me calling you either Dr. Jekyll or Dr. Frankenstein?"

"We do not use such treatment as straight jackets here. Ingesting a pill is more relevant. Not to mention, far more common."

"A pill. Like candy for an adult? A bomb of sense on a tongue or down the throat?"

"Adults don't play with metaphors in matters like these; if the pills you will have to take are symbolic, they represent advances in medicine. Do you *want* to be a chemical mishap?"

"Look, I am hearing voices and I think that there is something important in them. I am convinced there is a kind of knowledge in suffering, though I realize this may only hold up artistically and not scientifically. Suffering data would be counter-productive—would it not? You might want to know I wrote a poem about suffering in a bureaucratic style. Giving suffering a dignity and meaning is something that is going to be difficult. Why not, when science is like a Prozac commercial? It distils our tears backwards."

Institutional Courtyard: Scene

Homiletic of a space between clouds.
God has put the plants, the children, and the sky all to bed
but us to sick bed. The nightmare distils like a leaking faucet.

But, sitting there, I dreamt the argument that the courtyard was a sudden interior with a glass dome that updates Walter Benjamin's arcade. It suggests with its misaligned windows a composite introspection, a surprise, as a bug's-eye registers in a human mind, would register, not to mention a crowded feeling of things that don't actually have to deal with each other.

How to Defeat a Rubik's Cube, According to Jenna

There are *real, circular problems out there* to solve, like poverty and addiction… imagine a person addicted to Rubik's cubes. But if depression hands you a grey day, the Rubik's cube is easy to solve, all colours have become that hue. I noted that for Jenna there was an idiosyncratic aura to everything, and that it showed her idea of depth beneath surface complexity. But this is a parable of how mental illness can remind of the vastness of the world's problems, as we struggle infinitely with our own little problems, dismayingly similar to a series of walls or windows that seem to have trapped children behind them.

Betty's Text as a Boundary/ A Small Trap and Escape

Betty, her tone 'gentle,' often frazzled. A birdlike precision. Her voice a sharpened squeak sweeter than she would like to admit. She held out her arm and said, "I just read that 'touch has memory.'" Her intense look. Seemed to be playing a game. I had given her a book of poems from whence she derived the title. Rolling up her sleeve, she revealed the wounds. "Can you read them?" She explained that I should close my eyes and touch them, gently. I finally do but she makes a painful sound: I retract. She says, "your Braille is weak; you should read 'I am one of those proud sado-mason's people.'" She seemed pleased with the malapropism. "I swore that I could read 'just kidding' at the end," I say, defensively. "Or was it that I didn't read long enough? Everyone is a sadist...." In a pout she went over the first part of the wounds, and I thought back to the text on my wall. Does she live in "sadness," according to my wall, pretending to be a child? Her eyes looked like the braille of a tender illustration.

Visit: A Colonizer—Betty's Boyfriend

Untranslatable sketch of the con artist as an unconscious Jungian.
     Archetype of failure fading into dirt.
An implosive heart that breathes for other's blood
clings by his tattoo so that his image is stronger
  with thermometer veins
and a watch for participating on "Wheel
        of Fortune"... I've seen him alone with his aura
and parasitic handshake
     that has movement like he practised killing eels.
   "Hey, your fuckin' arm looks like shit, but let's go—hurry up!"
  Black smith of her nervous system,
    was she hurt by *the-loss-of-gentle-touch-all-at-once*

(that is his euphemism for "a punch")
when the music of the spheres is the sound of rocks
crashing the tapes that should soothe, now reel?
    He seemed impatient as if failure were a ceremony
    he needed to lead.

Journal Report from Group: Milton

"I have a clear reading of Dante's *Inferno* in which a character, encountering the absolute limit of the whole freakin' cesspool, discovers that the crazies live at the broadest circle of hell, and are hence perceptive of all of its tortures, which is why we stare so often. In my vision, the mad could be heard by providing a perfect representation of their suffering, with all the right feeling and brains. However, the general stupid curiosity of people sends them straight to hell. I don't know if this emphasizes listening to 'the voices' but it sure makes me tell people to go to hell!" I envisioned those of us who are most ritualistic hearing the term *obsessive compulsive* spoken like a mantra.

Almost the Eraser Dream Again

Tonight I heard Allison's voice with the nurse's. "Who will come for me?" "Your family." "They have been erased… they look like archetypes of everybody's child's drawings eaten away by the blank page." "But they are alive." I decided to enter the New Journalist phase as suddenly we were in medias res. Is it fair to listen? For either of us? An emotion I would have to discuss with the Nurse, unable to shake the idea that Milton (had just) suggested.

4) (Continued from notes near *A River of Logic Melting*.) "Can we silence words by writing them down?" Substituting "voices" for "words" allowed me to write the following:

Apostrophe in an Almost Empty Room/ Lines Reaching Out

Who, among medical staff or patients, would come to me first if I screamed "there are no angels left?" Angst is greed in my gaping dream; an eye refuses to blink.

Imagine if there were no membranes, walls, editors, or even the idea of focus.

How shall I compare thee to an empty room/ right as you enter it?
Kissed by erosion, time drifts in with its cloudy rabble and one prays decadence will be soft.

The pre-face is imperative in the eyes but subjunctive of the smile: muse of depression!

You water-coloured fairy always fainting, what drips do you fall for, you and your canvassing soul? To go beyond representation is to find shame in a mediocre adaptation of *The Divine Comedy*. And yet hell is boredom, a room filled with no one. Empty space is almost impossible to personify and no one wants to go with Dante or to be led by T.S. Eliot into a forest that might still seem empty. Yet, gushingly, you open your mind to other people you don't completely trust, those who have recently moved into your brain. A possible masterpiece of dissonance… I sleep in a pale vision of hell, told by a drifter, whose movement barely stirs a dream's energy so that I wonder if it will in fact just be in a limbo…

Nurse: The Attempt to Make a Coping Machine with a Lucid
Dream

You attend to the metaphysical black cats in your dream
weaving death's shawl and a voice blows out your candles with
    onomatopoeic oomph.
The cold will send numbness, its diplomat. The moon pressed into a
    pill to dream day
and you are born again with every loving gesture,
your renaissance ability.

One evening you discover a cat
has abandoned you/ you can tell this is a nightmare because of the way
you have always stood over the labyrinths of feeling
… and so you rush outside and there is a strange machine
that provides the darkness for some so that shame
in the city can find sleep from its prostitution-constitutions
its ladder-day superstitions, treatises that tease,
and distant meditations on inertia
in the same convention hall for lectures
on boredom for prone insomniacs, and supposed
victims refined or destroyed by Darwinist principles.

It is a "sigh-borg" able to produce oxygen and
appreciate poetry in the same breath. You make a cat shape
in the shadow where dawn will first break through the cracks.
And yet the thing that remains is the idea of a God of privacy
watching over the borders of sheer distance/ keeping
the mysteries between humanity fresh.

A New Context for an Epiphany: A New Space for a Coping
Machine

1.
A seeming calm: noise runs away from itself aware
of images assembled by something alien.
Silence, you think, is the only safety, and yet you
settle a vessel and touch the water, its beauty
a scream trapped in languid clarity. Into a haiku space you go;
a haiku that inspired first one, which for pedantic reasons
would not be:

"Mother nature leaves
her artery in the bark:
a wolf blends with trees."

And more like:

"The flowers bend to
sanction the wind's pleasant pass
yet you want to howl."

At the centre of a tree is a heart slow enough to love
me for minute nature poetry that has tried to be quiet.
A twig of mother nature's wind-speak: hush…
If there are gradations of a dream, the dream that is protected
must have no walls to restrict vision; even connotation can enter.
But a man in a boat on the lake, fishing, adorned with
simplicity, is a good start. Could be an
Ernest Hemingway exercise in nirvana.
The line is silver-cast in faint bug static.
There are voices of various wavelengths:
the whisper somehow lasts forever; a scream diffused,
a question to be a question; there is some voice without origin.

2.

From the vasty deeps, I eventually pull out a surrealist fish
which in this dream is a normal looking fish and all I can notice
is the way its mouth is so literal about breath: *memento mori.*
The haiku is a connect-the-dots game
ripped from the stars and looking its way yearningly,
I feel somewhere between heaven,
the man-made, and nature... can you feel it?
Like a strange colour green/ a cloud and a roof.

Journal: Reflecting on above Meditation

Depth is suspect hence a new mantra: as long is there is
beauty, surface is substantial and thus safe. A "veneerial disease"
begins; the fear and reliance on surface; a genital disease for the eyes.
"The sense of trusting what you see," Milton Phoenix would say, "gets
fucked in going nuts with tons of residual effects."

*

Last night; a country/blues song sobbed: "last night I saw my hat
it was a dome for your red shoe/ but you'd changed religion you've
gone to the blue."

Lullaby of the Sick:
"Somewhere under the Rainbow We Look Up..."

1.
How can we sing to you? In what feeble voice cracking?
Desperation in and out we are
squinting in the eyes of reduction, sought
like ants barely able to carry the weight of thought
we lift incredible burdens, dreaming sails. But
a baroque implosion feeds on sunflower seeds; we go looking
for the vegetable within to find our own spat-down light.
You see us mumbling, in the courtyard, procrastinating,
               a solo voice liking a John Cage scream.

*My voice is so open it gapes; a violin solo makes me think of a fake vein
and then of thunderbolt mauling it, without light or music.*

2.
An opera in which our voice's range
violates the paradox of Zeno
and our shrinking away. So we talk over noise,
but under sense, and its meanings
where shadows (ever so parenthetical) are
caught by radar. What a philosopher would see:
our thoughts are noisy toys you would discard.

3.
We sing the almost rocking bed its swing
from mania to not feeling even a fickle thing
and the idea of birds in the skies of memory
in the heart re-think, romantic, the wing
(in our pathological purse of coinage jingling).
In mania opera we cry out.
The things we think might exist include germs—

that odyssey to find yourself and children who never ask why?
The sky is a place where the sun never learns
all the other stars grew up and went away.
Leaves us slavish day to day.

Vignette: An Early Incident of Their Vicariousness

You moved toward the sound of your voice. It was calling the
suicide line, ridiculous in a hospital, but this only sinks in later.
Stilled, you listened. She was laughing or crying, saying that she had
already "opened her veins," but as you looked around the corner
her arms were free and unstained despite her sobbing. Earlier you
had said to her that you yourself were always *doing a bad impression
of an ideal self.* "I am dying as who was," she said in my voice, then
returning to her own: "but your *becoming* self cannot be a bad
impression, by definition." As she speaks, she turns around to face
you, putting the phone back on its hook. I understood; she killed
that part of me that was not being heard and the old self I was
ashamed of so that I did not have to do it, a vicarious gesture. I could
not help thinking of what Rick said about zombies and the idea of
appropriation. We might be too easily represented as mentally ill by
those who are not ill that way. If sadness is left alone too long and
gets clogged, it becomes anger.

Major Report: Addressed to Doctor Ludwig Earwinker

The patient Colin Verbanofsky has made an unusual regression and is hallucinating... he has constantly alluded to the presence of an Uncle Charles, and as we have been unable to discover someone by that name in his family, nor has this individual been here to see him... and besides he has spoken of people in an empty room... we wonder over previous diagnosis leads...

Re-Issue Report

Verbanofsky has explained that the"Uncle Charles principal" is a literary term. He believes in this, according to his testimony in the presence of the recently appointed Doctor Earwinker. As narrative moves figuratively closer to a character's mind, it takes on the idiosyncratic manner of thinking that the person has. So as our diagnosis moves nearer the patient, it should become as semantically discombobulated as the term 'schizophrenia' sounds, to be accurate, a disease which he says he thinks he has. With a glazed look he mentioned "deconstruction," which sounds highly degenerative... have been unable to find this in rare-diseases books. Diagnosis is still pending as many possibilities seem open.

More of a Dialectic than Previous Doctor Dialogue
Doctor Earwinker, coyly named as being "hard of hearing." He is known
to have callous ears from so much listening. He often said "blasted" as an
emphatic word.

Gently, the Doctor directed me to my seat, as he gathered his
mild bulk into a brown leather chair. He sat across from me behind
a palatial desk. He drew a heavy breath, looking somewhat weary.
Suddenly he stated: "Well, I understand that you have issues with
some of our procedures, 'that the instruments we have do not agree.'
You find our science here a bit dry. Or, perhaps, possessing a bad
chemistry." He held his pen like a small shovel. I was caught off
guard by his mention of Auden but recovered as quickly as I could.
"Ur, yes." I said. 'I mean, yes. Exactly. I am doing work of my own
that might interest you. For example in my studies of patients I, too,
have begun to suspect a new language is needed and that many of
your diagnostic terms are fundamentally though ironically flawed."
The Doctor frowned as if considerately, and nodded. "I see," he said
over a careful distance, and added: "I have read the reports and
have been following you—your case. Your central concern is that
there is a representational problem, of which you"—he paused as if
ceremoniously giving credit— "see as a core issue of being here." A
clear re-wording of my more convoluted explanations, yes, I silently
agreed, and nodded. Then, more closely, he said: "I also hear you
have not read Williams, but you have read Blake."
"I assume you planted it there for me," I said, immediately and
suspiciously, thinking of the library here. And then, with a gesture
not alien to comedy, he playfully hummed:

> "To see the world in your diagnosis
> but yourself in your doctor
> to see materialism in a thought
> and the conditions for good laughter."

He was playing with a stethoscope, which to him, I suspected, was a toy, perhaps a reference to Auden interpreted a little too literally for my tastes. After all, he was supposed to be a *psychiatrist*. Still there were more pressing questions.

"My question to you is this: what do you do with philosophic longing? It does not lend itself to your wish fulfilment. Last night I dreamt that Socrates' face floated up part by part from a strange Ouija board, and I realized ugliness is truth— he was supposedly quite ugly and he was here," I added needlessly.

"Well, the truth of your diagnosis might be ugly as well," he said, "though I dislike having to inform you of this. Is this perhaps your longing? It is quite possible that personification ends at illness. We know you mentioned a time of instant gratification. Could your illness being immediately defined—as by the pleasing of the eye—be an insult to your alleged depth?" This made me think of Jenna's way of seeing surfaces in a kind of cubist way of thought, as if things were transparent. It was a wake-up call. I need to consider things-in-themselves, a philosophic fantasy or perverse nightmare, a Ouija board of inhuman symbols floating upward like kites whose strings are to string theory what a star was before black holes: connections between things.

A Mural along the Borderline Split Person: Looking Back with New Perspective

The frame so severe that its application
tore the thin painting whose image was incidental...
Like a faint statement on one's death bed
with ironically precise decorum...
Water-coloured diffusion and a ship spilled oil the canvas sails away
and you think of method... snail action painting
complicates the idea
of abstract expressionism...
The frame will endure unless you can
recall how the story fell apart...
At the centre of the canvas is a door and if you believe
in perspective it would open   get the background
of its dimension and history and yet in literature
one's main perspective is different   precisely not in the
(distance)
except in time. But emerging from your vernacular, if your
perspective were that of art's, however, placing you would be as
difficult as placing me. But how, how to make a composition of this
mess of me splattered? Opening doors of hospital... I am looking at
this frame, the last one I held and it might just be art: on the frame I
imagined how my plight of hieroglyphs in a dark room would look
a stick figure inflated now between heart and head or the swirls of
wind like Doric dust and how I flowed to the hospital almost a siren
in my wrists.... And now I rest in canvas-white rooms re-thinking
the dove. The whole universe is upside down; the doves are upside
down. Your strangest visions cannot be read so easily o agency my
captain you realize your perspective; your author*ship* sails back into
the painting of night spilled and you begin to move on as abstractions
thicken/ without myth the story is stricken.

Critique of Creativity: Reflective Re-Write on a Quantitative Essay Partially Written before Breakdown that Led to Hospital: Degree of Madness: Accurate

I wanted to write an ultimate "quantitative" essay that would criticize "creativity"; though this would not have been possible when the latter term was associated with God. It would go against all systems—teleology, church, creation itself. If things began to change too much, this could be a way of saying that God had done too well, i.e., s/he or it had produced a fertility that was endlessly generative, within which the created could do likewise. I ended up saying that the problem with *artists* is that they are poster boy and girl messengers of philosophy. Rather than engage in the usual pacing and chin-grabbing, the artist had to deeply inhale the outdoor air and then vomit it in a metaphor of expression. "If it is art, boundaries must be broken" goes the current general argument. And indeed they would be like the cages of Blake's "The Tyger," the boundaries, that is. To trap a colour that is tiger-like, you need an all-purpose frame. Creativity is inherently irresponsible. *A conservative God would have only had to **whisper** genesis.* That was my basic argument. My idea was ingeniously reductive; creativity simply gives us too much un-likely-ness. I realized that others would suppose that this was a parody of a mathematician's reductive claim. Yet math is far more universal.

Despite accusations of minimalism of life, complication is a survival tactic for most bureaucracies. I would argue the voice of God could have been perfect and that there was a lovely moderation whose duration would have been longer, and there would thus be no need for bureaucracy to slow this down, although my job was a nice moderation between. The artists, through exaggeration, inflate expectation too high by borrowing—or stealing—the word "create."'

This moderate God I mentioned is what I want to believe in. For practical and absurd reasons the artist and bureaucrat are always in a state of separation. Artists were, in biological terms, often like bad mothers; they brought something new into the world, yes, but nothing more than a mewling puking thing, an object that never grows up, an elaborate toy for endless play.

Creativity is useful only as a rhetorical word. It excites us to the glorifiable obscure. I allow that, relatively speaking, there have been creative people, but their collective efforts can be best as seen as confusing things without the clarification of philosophy. What is cubism but an irrepressible greed for instant gratification, getting all false angles at once like a bad journalist? The idea of the moment in modernism should have seen postmodernism coming and cubism merely speeded up impressionism because you make things last less long if they are exposed all at once. Expressionism's projection of feeling is the failure of a telescope and an indulgent emotional singularity; if everything felt like you did, through your feelings colouring the world, at any moment boredom would rule the universe until something would snap, leading to fauvism. Impressionists are weak indecisive expressionists: And so it would go on. Yet all of this was beginning to sound both hollow and too simple as if I were thinking too much about surface.

Report on Patient Colin Verbanofsky

The patient insists we write down that "in the time of fallen metanarratives, genius is the last bombastic *single word* that could rejuvenate the story that will replace these overarching stories. The story of every-person who thinks that a "crazy" person believes a giant conspiracy that explains their every move, suggests madness is a remaining example of metanarrative that we see as moments…."

Report Continued...

Rick Genevive suggested to the patient that his Broca's region was connected unusually to his emotional register, in trying to explain his intense feelings about language. This at first angered the patient but, as the statement sunk in, he grew thoughtful about the idea. Nurse Vella—who has become quite close with the patient—has noted a central problem of Verbanofsky's, that his imagination is both complex and complicating; *his is the Hamlet imagination with little to do.* She thinks this could be the product of all the reading he did. Yet he remains very studious, and has persisted in exposing several patients to literature, going so far as to make a card that says: "it is my business to create."

A Dream of Madness/ A Kind of Strategy

... The former supposedly avoids consequence. In it I am the madman and everything I say, every exclaimed utterance, matches perfectly with the Jabberwoken dream and its surreal traffic. It is important that I record it as a *particular* dream because it forces you to not consider me lost in the generality of madness, as if confusion has no precision.

In the dream I pass by Sigmund Freud, who is holding a cardboard sign that says he is "asking for change." He then appears before me and tells me that he desperately wants me to see his mind, a gesture that seems almost Dantean.

Then we are on a zig-zagging path in a car through wormy tunnels of the brain and we see an ambitious dream first-hand, and roadside ads for "life" for malls, like tame facades for westerns without the precision of guns, just exhaust pipes. There is a sense of the building of a system, though as I look carefully I see everyone here is Freud, a strange solipsism that suggests enslavement. Freud suddenly lies down on a psychiatrist's couch and I am a doctor and I find his brain has seeped down into the body. He asks me to tell him a story, but just then I awake much like a story of life, left with a question of what it would mean if Freud was in some sense insane. I might consider thinking of him more sympathetically. The question that I now face is how to tell this as a story, how images tell a story. The elliptical scenes suggested a poem that might in a story be a moment of doubt. Yet I realized that all the different people were in the shop house of my head, which now felt better for me for some reason. I worked hard to interpret this as not prophecy, but wish fulfilment.

In some poems, the elliptical is expected and yet I have here attempted prose because the world now has come to suspect the sweet nothings of poetry.

Hamlet the Dreamer

To go mad or dream; that is the question.
Whether 'tis nibbling at the mind to have
fingers point at you, diagnosing your
feelings of slings and arrows or to suck
all wounds with a pillow and end them for
a night in brain waves. To go mad is to
end the world of definite borders and
yet there is a dream of madness: where is
the rub on the betray'd dreamer's back? For
in the imagined sleep of all reason,
what fantasies might come? We shuffle off
the chains of mortal indignation and
think there is a pause as if a disease
would respect flesh, like a traveller at
the gates of a normal life's limit and
it would see the natural shocks of the
decent heart. Who would bear the suits and ties
to time in an office? The bosses' red
pen point, the prying man's open doors and
the police re imagine the laws, why
can we not? We can make quietness with
sleep but with madness there is always too
a noise as some food has no knife or a
violin but the fear that in madness
there is still a boredom when tedium
makes us sweat and grunt into a dull life;
the dread of a bureaucracy in the
brain where the messages are logic dis-
prov'd and band aid stick-it notes: art on walls.
This hiding makes coward consciousness
band-aid's skin colour as one hue of a
resolution. But mind sickness has too

black and white and the enterprise of a
curveball pitch the darkest of humours the
current logic washes Ophelia
away.

Biographical Note and Critique of Mind
Inside Hamlet's Mind Is a Quote by Nietzsche:

*"A nerve-stimulus, first transcribed... into an image...! First metaphor!
The image again copied into a sound! Second metaphor!"*
                                        —*xxii Of Grammatology*

Hamlet's graveyard scene could include a critique of the idea that the mind is as literal as bone. That is why he hesitated about acting; if the mind were a mere organ of thought in which dwelt "merer" images, romanticism would never have been born. The brain as slap stick would much resemble Hamlet's dumb show: what is the most eloquent verb he'd use in an anachronistic reading? Heidegger's being?

If in the above soliloquy, where he is the universal Hamlet, we could suggest that he knew his actions and not just his thought would have to be perceived as for all of us, giving him almost the grandeur he might need to shuffle away Claudius. Would this betray his mind-based identity?

"... Look you, this brave o'erhanging firmament, this majestical roof fretted with golden fire, why, it appeareth nothing to me but a foul and pestilent congregation of vapours."
                                        —*Hamlet*, Act 2 Scene 2 lines 302-305.

The Dead Star Light Centred Generation: Chemical Soul
Critique Continuing with Hamlet's Mind Critique/ The Moon as
a Pill for a Misdiagnosis

Picture a psychedelic moon: (in a children's-
book universe: illustration of limit).
Note our pot-hole shoes!
We, the Braille semioticians of how-to vectors
of rhetorical emptiness endless
as bombast of agoraphobia love of
small closures is the moon sealed until you see it
follow footprints of the explicit ones, their rocky road touch
as if wind on snow—or blow—eradicated each imprint.
But what do you call the culture of the moon's blues
centred instead on a dead star helium-centtrick light glimmer
of knowledge like a star that has been dead for years
squinting and growing dimmer.
Leprous moon cells more alone as marrow-less
bone. That full-of-itself moon
hung like a note/ rock music of the spheres/ a pill is a question
                        chemical reactions are answers, in effect...
"Can you represent me?" A drug trip sets this
question in languid water... the lava lamp as shrine.

Everyone Listens as if to Music
A Polyphonic Poem

Ironically, Sal was also known as "the silent one." He quietly
walked into the room where we rested, and immortally talked his
way out, becoming a kind of saint. He said: "I know what Mozart was
thinking and feeling when he composed a (or any) particular piece."

"Mozart endured some terrible things: an atypical
    childhood, disease and the loss of many children.
           But he spoke transcendent child; An improbable toy
  vacuum lay forgotten by his side though his instruments seem
           to not exist—but is God perforating the clouds,
      haloing Mozart's cloudy wig, dizzy awe
       but the notes hold you with precision and embrace, astound.
You think of snow falling in ubiquitous sighs and an impossible
rust-proof phonetic-mobile wind-chime all in one."

"We cannot imagine the layman playing air violin to
    express the intangible in Mozart that somehow
is tangible through him.
       If Mozart were simple and literal he might have
chords of high
      notes in an archipelago grasping happiness, say."

"Sure, he was in ecstasy when he wrote
    Eine Kleine Nachtmusik music—certainly declarative melody,
    and he was probably thinking about God at some
          point during *Requiem*, but…"

"I remember, a night after missing medication
for several days, but not fully removed from panic's explosive eyes
to lessen my mother's concern, I put on
     some of Mozart's music while looking romantically
     out the window announcing that I knew what Mozart
     was feeling. My mother reminded me that I did this
          when I was sickest... I had forgotten this note, or fact."

"The work I had chosen was the overture from *The Magic Flute*.
     The one with the big bangs, as Genesis might have.
But then, a violin weaves a subtle ingenious way out. A
flight of the bumble-bee flying ornately in Vivaldi's
     spring so fancy free trolls would dance as if to a Chopin waltz.
Mozart knew the way out of melancholia; and he smuggled it
          in a *violin*; who would suspect?! The irony!"

"Yet, a strange music all my own occurs when I think
          how others assume me incapable of such music.
Though it is true, I am to Mozart what noise is to music..."

"But when no music is near, I am still convinced
     I have wrestled a possible silence that is perhaps not as
great as the one Mozart faced. But we all wrestle with silence,
a censor that has no voice. How long can one stand mime opera?
     Mozart was so cooperative he did not slaughter silence, but
          gave it a space in the frame-work of music, giving us a strange
          poetic licence."

I could not help but wonder if that would be possible
for all of our voices.
Silence is not simply waste in music.
I had pictured classical music as now being dream catchers,
thrown in dumps,
that were records of the everyman yawning at the opera.

Journal and an Act of Privacy

I wrote the following poem after Allison and I had spent the day together. I had told her that her truant memory was in fact enabling in putting her into a perpetual balance between the "death of the author" and the "birth of the reader." "A pop-up book for new young mother written anonymously?" she asked, already conceiving of its cover. (Her attempts to construct the universe prevented her from being a fish in a bowl, she explained. Yet, sometimes only a detail, like a fishbowl, helped her distinguish time and space). My arcane theory took some explanation, but she soon seemed to have a grasp of the subject. As we talked she told me it was only her same form that allowed her to know that she was not someone, or something, else. I realized that her imagination was too powerful for much of this world and that her equilibrium was thus distorting her memory. We seemed to possess a child's elegy. I would devote a great deal of time to her that I do not record in these notes.

The Re-Consideration of Wit from the *Vision of Sadness*

The first thing uttered by the inter-text machine
after hearing a million questions
at a news conference, was the name of its favourite
author: "Anonymous"
        - Intertext. (Quoted exactly as such
in the newspapers of tomorrow).
The next day the word "author" was found
picture-less, in the obituary, though a shape-shifty-sounding
person wrote an editorial signed
"A Formalist" (another anonymous witty response, perhaps),
wondering if "dead metaphor" was related to the
    author, deceased. At the conference

a very human, i.e., compassionate-looking media reporter,
stood up and asked if now all "authors are
now not anonymous?" "Dead metaphor, left behind,
is allegory wake," the machine said.
The audience sighed much static.
At that point, appropriation stood up and asked
a question for everyone... No one objected.

As a "Madman" I am still anonymous.
As if mad/ man were just another word in a constructed landscape.

With Vorseth and the Torture of Time

"If Proust began with the smell of marijuana in *Swann's Way*... he
would evoke our sickness: beat literature, mascara-veined emo-
vampire with empty supermodel eyes, instead of health's image:
a credit-card-organ'd self-polished-endorsement-of-disguised-
hedonism able to scavenge fashion with the reflexes of a predator,
who feels that all things were meant for him, yet carries no baggage.
Do we not get lost in this smoke? And we blur inversely. Our souls
the image of each other; we think they have dark evil souls and they
think we are pleasure-seeking in some lesser way, that we just don't
understand basic happiness. Then what of us in a hospital? How
well do you remember your past, pre-hospital?" he asked. I said
something brief but then wrote the following.

When Sarcasm Was the Only Irony: A Renaissance Repression/ Or, the Word "Cool" in an Abridged Thesaurus: Not at Homage with Mary

In high school, acting was a role so fundamentally essential that it rose conspirator-like above the theatre department into the mountains and valleys of shrugs and disregard, using sarcasm which the face so eloquently represents. Yet the definition of acting was slang-applicable as a prefix and I would become a calloused person myself for a change, acting less sensitively. The icy universe became known as "cool." For me this temperature would occur one afternoon when I first moved into the city. Once trapped in openness, I was now having to embrace claustrophobia's conformist shuffles.

One day after English class, I happened upon the bigger boys who were in the same class on a smoke break, always an odd act of catharsis from one's own life. But of course this was a ritual, accompanied by a strange informal god from the machine, a God of indifferent transactions. The Sistine Cigarette. The enigmatic phrase "whatever" seemed to sanctify vagueness with a flourish of camouflage, and a hyphen bridge across humanity, enabled all things to be like Occam's razor, seemingly an object in the anthropology phase of science class. Their mostly dumbed-down faces conveyed the idea that a generality was religious.

The topic of poetry came up in a kind of humorous way, or, at least from my perspective. A gruff voice began: "They are speaking *gib* or whatever you call it. I think Shakespeare is taught because it sounds cool. Or whatever big word Mr. Ventrilico would use."

"Cool to him, you mean?" I asked, attempting a small act of translation.

"Whatever." He looked away, far too silvery for my boyish sunshine.

"He thinks he is the boss," another voice said, this one belonging to a much larger fellow.

"Lear?" I asked, trying a small door of perception into his mind.

"No, Mr. Ventrilico. That's why we have to learn it. Because of him, *he* thinks it's important, or something."

"I don't mean to sound *every centimetre* a clown defender of poetry, but wouldn't it make more sense if he were to use some kind of literature that would get us interested and would slowly take over our minds? He can tell we are uninterested, but he does not seem to take pleasure in this fact. That is the job of science teachers." I laughed nervously and looked around. The cigarette had avoided my direction, and my successful amusement was a million miles away. A lynched muse.

Their tallness deemed them transcendent, and yet, as I noted the smell, I realized it was a pharmaceutical: pot! My face must have betrayed me. I was aghast when I spilled my expression, "is that *marijuana?*" in a voice a lot louder than was required for my bit part in the social encounter.

"Poetry." One of them said— "we like to refer to it as a joint. That is the *term*." He sounded scolding, and this was one of the boys who was actually quite smart, I realized, and he was the aerodynamically-faced sports guy possessing a kind of masculine credibility I could never have. Or so I felt with my usual intimations of failure. The boys finished the joint and tossed it down, as a group, I thought, a small bone with magical marrow. Now, leprous, a worm sucked into the body, memento mori. They used a conjunction to exclude me was the irony—a joint—and yet my sarcasm did not join. I felt the line where Cordelia says, "I cannot heave my heart into my mouth." That was my predicament. I was beginning to fathom my little spongy heart and for me a conjunction was, ironically, theatrical: it was *and...?* expecting more. But "and" is also able to connect almost anything; it constructs the universe.

The prefix 'un' became an identity. I became unlike those others I had encountered that day. A bureaucrat has an un-life. A RE-UN LIFE. Who would have suspected a chemical imbalance would

provide an undoing on both ends of time? Instead of an abridged
thesaurus I wished I'd had the pocket-sized dictionary of wit, a book
of faith for these generality-thinking guys. Opening it on any page
would result in my triumph. I still recall their eyes, glazed as donuts,
as I cracked it open, risking a chance. Remember their mouths
hardened partly open when my finger fell on the word "disconnect,"
it said. To "dis"—an insult.

How to Make a Visionary: While Staring at Another Person Starring Vorseth upon My Retelling of the Above Story and a Pledge of Language

I seek the essence of brevity/the purity of pith!
With a stealth satellite of universe drift
our voices collect wit like magpies in reels of sky, screwing stars
    into the sockets some call black holes. Life is no joke, but hey,
how many sperm does it take to screw in a light-bulb?
A hippie consults astronomy while the sperms confuse
this for a knock-knock joke, striking the bulb repeatedly
        to the best of their knowledge trying to get inside
to answer the question… not knowing their existential fate.
    An egg as an image is intellectual minimalism.

Your blink eating a tear rapacious looking up to holey light/ rose
an aneurysm of beauty, an aesthetic wink, in the vein-flooded eye.
(The eye that looks unerringly like a deflated whoopee cushion closes
tighter than a cabbage). A coping mechanism is not
an agen bit of inwit:
nor is it a dream machine with a comforting voice.
Until you speak of it too often it repeats judgements with a delicate
    hammer.   The moment is an
overexposed photo, a single judgement can make a blink a seal.

In my thinking I have realized Nietzsche's synapse
imagined in Hamlet's head. Light: it jumps, paces, pushes,
asks as if it were trapped... This beam's almost onomatopoeia;
a Genesis in the verb of being and wanting to be more. Howl is the
    right word...
The vowel rings like a star with consonants forging it into a beam.

The butterfly moment of beauty and you have two possibilities:
pin point its fleetingness or, like a Neanderthal,
look at your fingernail
and make it sharper and pin it down literally.
I am going deeper into your voices, I thought,
as you see I chose giving birth to a voice as a metaphor in a single chip.
A foetus falls away, but personification is at the heart of my search.

It is my belief in your voices, my acceptance
of your *sincerity* that makes me think I can pull up
a new formula for gravity letting go of art's appearances
to drift amid kites of the insane: it is not any absolutism that gives me
    this belief. But
if your voices were not in some sense real... I could not do this.
            If a band-aid were a label, we'd bleed through it beautifully.
Politically correct angels whose emanations
are environmentally friendly
and whose body types, neither fat nor skinny, descend. But

All the universe is a theatre! And all humans merely alien(ated).

Visitor Frank Newman: A Distinguished Asshole Lacking Anal-Retentive Polish/

The Author Realizes He Truly Prefers Patients to Outsiders

Frank answers the question, "how do we sing to you?" in an earlier poem, the answer being: with an old ballad in the heavy metal genre.

"Hey, ... I heard you have been doing that rhyming shit. No wonder no one talked to you at work, hey? So, like, what happened anyway?" (I considered the ballad form almost immediately and yet could not think of a line to quote. I heard Milton outside the door, speaking to Allison, as experience and imagination in a small lecture hall. How to explain the ways of complexity to someone who in *Inferno* would have probably been punished for gluttony and for self-flattery, all his senses covered in filth.... I tried to picture this with as much clarity as possible, but just in time I realized I might look delusional doing so extendedly by the pleasant feeling I would get on my face from this elaborate torture. I raised my eyes to his low brow with waves of hair.)

"Oh, not much, I just needed a rest. How is the old office?" I spoke a
    straight frame.

I managed to speak three more subsequently and with no content as
    a tribute to our work days.

Critic of Emotions: A Role to Replace Mere Coping
Mechanisms

1.

Ostensibly, a "critic" seems to be a snob incapable of experiencing
un mixed emotions; nothing short of canonization could make
them "happy." They sit with forever-folded arms like a machine
with too many buttons. The same is true for the depressive, except
s/he is a living embodiment of criticism. Everyone else, relatively,
is (read *feels*) like an artist, living expressively. You watch perfect
con men reach for cappuccino cups as if they were God's models.
A handyman, the depressive thinks, who will find grace in arthritis
and pose for the abstract statue of a statistic as if he were hunted by
Hollywood spotlights. But if this could be translated to a feeling;
ah, how complex! There are the toweringly indifferent-to-others'-
feelings people to be aware of. They are the statues that got away the
sheer forces of youth to whom shadow is just getting in their light.
And so when you become a critic of feeling through depression, the
worst is the black and white movie about the corroded rainbows you
have to watch in your documentary about your own introspection
and acting. While you talk about a movie you feel the editing out of
gratuitous fatty thought and blackness. A curtain and a reel make for
terrifying theatre, and all foreshadowing is equivalent to paranoia in
this image-world.

Yet, you become incredibly sensitive.

2.

Be the relocated blind person in the famous elephant parable except here, you are sightless and going through the things in Van Gogh's room, rather than touching different parts of that animal. If you touch his bed first you might think of the malaise'd laziness of artists in general and their priorities.

You might touch his little chair and think that it stood for something or that it was wobbly to flatter him if he were drunk, and yet most intoxicating was a painting leaning in the corner. It had a kind of energy that would not be seen again until Jackson Pollock. You could feel that he had made something better than a window, because the stars he painted were like Keats's but that clearly the sky had fallen and perhaps this modest frame was all that prevented the sky from trickling across the floor, which a painted sky must never do.

But we cannot limit our synesthesia to just *feeling blue* now, can we?

Try tasting the lack of touch which stinks of silence and the watching colours sound like a red scream which tastes of the texture in thick goblety blood. Fill in the blank what is touch-less-ness that feels like every taste of blasphemy that your feeling gives the smell: a baptism of sweat. All of this could exist in "blue."

How to Make a Movie Influenced by Robert Graves's "In Broken Images."
Witticisms by Jenna that Argue against the Pleasant Image Language of Science

1.
"Where is meaning?" asked the drooling hunter.
"Right here," pointed near, a language anti-wonderer.
"From whence are you both?" queried everyone's mother.
This seemed an ideal spot for a good bad movie.

2.
A drawing image of an erect penis
too large to fit into arcane artistic categories.
"C'est ne pas un penis."
Or, "This is not *your* penis…"

3.
Reality is a question of visibility; Hollywood
teaches this; the reason for things hiding
is the Hallmark card you cannot find.
"It's somewhere in the metaphysical section, as *you* would say,"
she said to me. Feeling replaces reality. Expressionist vortex.

4.
Love at first sight requires an x-ray in
the science fiction of today, and in Victorian times
lust would be out of the picture, politely.
The word *shape* spoken flatly.

5.
Diagnosis at first blink/ love at first look away.

6.
Transparency is a form of freedom, if you are a window.
Opaqueness is the freedom to choose ambivalence.
Darkness is a dead metaphor, being eroded.
Beyond, of course, is light that sees the dark…
… as clearly as the dark sees itself.

Vignette with Jack Being a Visionary in Words

Since his exposure to the idea that he exists in relativist space
(the centre is where you are) and is only one centre, he has become
adamant that his language is simply too great; *there is no way I could
live up to it.* Upon his requesting my writing him an ode, I retort:
how could I mimic his great voice? Luckily, he is feeling explanatory:

1) Your tone needs to seem absolute, even as a first impression.
   Rhetoric and performativity: find a code between.

2) Your reach and grasp need shake hands where others cannot see
   them do so.

3) You must have a trace of all the great systems but use the word
   "individual" constantly.

NEW SECTION Colin Is De Centered, Too
Official Hospital Document: Report of Sorts

"It has been decided in a unanimous vote by all levels of hospital staff that for one evening, the beds of all the patients will be placed in a circle, then allowed to engage in a form of discourse for a short proximity of time, before the lights will be turned out and they will be instructed to sleep. The experiment is two-fold: one, to see how their conscious voices operate in relation to each other, and two, to see how these voices will affect their dream lives… The patient Colin Verbanofsky made the suggestion…"
Signed

. . . .

Earlier the Day of/ Evoking a Bricolage Universe: Morning
Before

1.
In the *medias* res of morning
                    and love's prospects drooped
I wear black and I imagine star light
collapses into my William Carlos Williams coffee cup
            and think of onion unpack-able constellations—
    all because I forgot sugar. Hence another sweet nothing
has been added
        to the universe. The bombasted snowflake turns
contrivance like a factory.
    And, as Yeats once said "All changed, changed utterly."
        It was a poem that created autumn even though "green is worn."

2.
I am praying for logical clarity, but the voice of irony
        is too clever to speak to me. It is
the brilliant kid w. broken glasses
            whose father is an astrologist at Oxford—
        is he the voice of reason? A
    pretentious being, monotone worldly.
                Instead of a "herd of onions headed for the head"
            as Rick joked we might see reason die, falling from
    a high horse that a poem said started autumn/ the hot hooves
striking the turning leaves.

Literary Fantasy: What Impossible Sonnet Was in Frame, This Is in Content

It seemed logical; if "there are still songs to
sing beyond mankind," why are we solely flooded
with feelings of sky? What of an infinite below,
where the too-curious explorers go? What if the sky
fell in childish sensation and amid teeming life
we could whim-pearl the minted pith of dream—
perfect poetry that absolves the air with description.
I thought if I had the Mozart speech in mind I
could find the strange rhythm at the heart of us,
even the most eccentric, and would not commit "the heresy of
paraphrase," but obey silence on my return, so that I
was not a *mere translator*, a shield deflecting misquotes,
with simulacra exposed. I would have *the* antecedent and
would see that its aura of perfect silence would speak
later, using time iambic ecstatic it would be raw
epiphany matter. This was the explanation of
Ginsberg's "symbols of themselves." Hence it would not
merely be description, as accused is literature, of being.
(Can we relax in the decorum of complexity?)
All the erased words will surface like wit
in the bubbly history of etymology one fine moment,
consult a deconstructive Sherlock-Tracy and everyone
would also find a heroic couplet in the fill-
in-the-blank-elegy within the haiku garden of perfection
where all is a metre high yet you can breathe over it... pufff!

Song of Open Beds: Recalled Dialogue Fragments

"I call all the voices: gargoyle of our edge, Milton, what do you see?"
"I see the bottom: my hand splayed this strange foundation…
a sort of synesthesia: a touching vision for the whole family of
pathologies."
"Is that our notion of surface? Seems like a measure of sorts."
"But can we think past mires of static
or any variation of impediment? The gravity here is *insane*."
"And can I survive when an eraser has been dragged,
like a glacier, over my memory though I barely recall the
touch?"
"Do you remember me from yesterday… and if I hold
a scream inside, will it grow like a baby?"
"Emotional growth like a converted tumour
melting in the throat.…"
"Why is there a feeling that shadows matter?"
"Yes, feelings *shadow* matter: our feelings flood static and
matter is as dumb
as a mannequin in a riot. Feelings seem to colour
things so negatively."
"No, no: why do we suspect the *relevance* of shadows? Why is
literal darkness
seeming to speak of curiosity's taboo fetish?"
"Why is the voice of hope so quiet?
I wonder if innocence can close its big eyes in time before it sees
everything? All that space to close.…"
"The glimmer congealed into pearl…
our reality is what then, shadows mining for ink? Ink
dripping tortuously?"
"Have you all not heard of performativity? Perhaps we can
affect our dreams by speaking in a specific way—?
Imagine if we found each other in a mass lucid dream."
"(and bruise those dreams with our splayed hands…

as we grope feebly?)"
"The voice of hope sounds like a perfect epitaph set silent on stone to
answer the question."
"We are not adventurers but escapists as we fall
into an evil of the imagination; that's what madness is.
And we its antiheroes."
"But it is my words that hold up the sky of this conversation."
"Can we really speak about some kind of fall into hell
that is an immortal monument of our conditions
—when our decline seems a mere trip and fall accident?
A biological blip in a chemical cesspool?"

Two Non Sequiturs After

Milton: "That conversation was not black enough to twentieth-
century standards of horror; this is only the psychedelic of "dark."
The psychedelic of dark: do you get it? Gone to the dark side like
a million stolen Jedi swords jammed into a brief case. All right, all
right, it is just a drug trip I had."

Betty: "What about God's belief in himself? What if that's why the
world is so bad? He is insecure, maybe, because no one believes in
him?"

Self-Written Report

Led by Milton, what followed was an argument that could have been a debate about the real existence of hell. There were traces of this place: human suffering and the archetype of institutions combined with the inability to imagine any happiness convincingly, as if it were an exotic condition. When Betty asked if innocence's big eyes would have time to close before they saw everything, it made me recall that sometimes, looking over a city, we have the opposite feeling one should have; with a great vista should come feelings of beautiful grandeur, vitalizing challenges and the idea of ruling. To that we have our countless isolationist spaces and they all add up to a condition of yearning for something metaphysical, like a great beyond. Who could govern this diffuse empire of abandoned connection, this tenuous acrobat pedestrian-ism? And in our hell there would be modification. In the theology of hell the damned never took solace in each other's presences, and it is only our mutual awareness of *concealed* suffering that complicates hell's implicitness/explicitness. Hell is other people with agoraphobia. The giving of pills could be a Dantean punishment that could give an illusion that you could imagine each pill making the previous one more beautiful and they become increasingly transparent just like your skin till you can see you have the same content as the pills. And in false haiku clarity (the enlightened paratactic) things become shiny, (really they were just incredibly slippery, eel unsealed), and it was ideal for Betty's eyes, as she cried beyond all clichés at the negativity of the rest of the dialogue that comprises the above poem, with a greater descent. This is the world just before an apocalypse, where all becomes an elaborate mistake and it is waiting to be washed down a gyre of a drain as the paratactic breaks in the way it hates the most. But we manifested a huge composite question to be posed against delusion and there were laws to it. When we speak at times it it is the poetry of the gut, like a mad scientist's tubes with the distilled spit resultant from the very sweat of alchemy, and it seemed as if the condition we lived in seemed to be more of a community again. It was as if we were stealing the questions from the psychiatrist who matches the aforementioned imagined archetypal institution.

A How to Make Delusion Guide: Unanswered Questions Become Answers as a Compromise after Open Beds Failure: A Parody of His Previous Delusional Optimism and Yet a New Epiphany

What exactly is delusion? The echo correcting you?
A severed intrusion/ that worms its way into the mind's
divided attention-span with a humming bird's wings,
arrives out of the blue. A truth tuned to temptation
that ever-opens. How do you think fire feels, turning to smoke?
Opaque epiphany like a blush! We are the ones who truly look
                         delusion
in the visage; this is our representational triumph.
Everyone else sees (the wrong verb entirely) what they *take*
to be delusion, but it is just an out-of-context thing,
like the humane bohemian revolting in cold hipster elitism/
delusional focus is like reading in the dark. Is it
                  fiction for the unconscious?
Expecting the sun we almost sang about will come
                down, an apparition
of a child's smiling sun that purges itself of hellfire/ vomiting light.
Can you see it? If so, consider this the data of delusion/ itself a
    delusion, doubled.

        Uncertain why it stands seemingly alone.

Futurist War Analogy as Allegory and Parable of Depressive Suffering

The prince's game (she-loves-me/ she-loves-me-not) makes one think they could coerce or slow down autumn. This game could also be applied to the flower's entirety, not only its petals, which I am tempted to say resemble the lapping tongues of a laughing god of many languages and one throat. The prince believed that beauty, like laughter, should permeate everything, ubiquitously. Hence, he glued the petals back, stuck them onto the roots because he saw no reason that the hidden should be overlooked as if from shame. He wore a Midas cross-of-arms on his shield and when aping with the children of his empire, he would say that his powers began at gold. To find his goal of total beauty, he needed to alleviate pain and speak of death as if it were a rumour by rhetorician. Death is falling apart, arid decadence, the opposite of beauty, *memento mori* as a *cliché*. He named his jester 'Anonymous' and gave him eggs to crack in juggling. His jester said he could see his prince doing the *she-loves-me/ she-loves-me* not routine with potpourri. There was laughter which reigned for a time.

Then it came one day—news that a war had descended in his land's furthest corner, a place he barely thought of. With a chivalrous voice the prince rose his neck and spoke to his trembling people, who were otherwise working to make all things gorgeous. "Somewhere deep in war will be a hidden beauty, a futurism," he said. And in terror he mounted his unicorn and went toward battle. And yet, he, a natural, realized that he too must rely on an extraordinary muse of war. A shaven Rapunzel lowered the canonical tower and charged with it! Akin to a harbour of blood, a highly dense rose was added to the generic green of the fields as he watched from above, on a cliff. Brimming with ecstasy he reached into his sachel, where he found his reconstructive flower. But in sudden loss a wind ripped all the petals away as if to say, "I lust you all." Then, he looked around and saw he was surrounded by blood-soaked enemies holding huge stinger-spears. The new army felt his massacre of the flower was irredeemable and his perversion of it even worse. As a result they locked him in a tower where he was to receive only bread and water. It overlooked a garden of *conventional* beauty, but he felt none of this, in its origins it was like pre-suffering beauty and did not permeate him whatsoever. In another hundred years, it was not hard to picture, another army would come to correct this one, indignant that *they* had invented the word *flower* and that according to their new and improved classification had recognized the first capturing army had in fact been worshipping a weed in the name of flora. The weed, the prince came to realize, symbolized the beautiful without moral goodness and it grew on his window sill in a plethora of tangles; he found them all the more stunning knowing they were weeds.

Because of the futurist vision of war the prince, whose beauty was deemed a simple universalism, found himself imprisoned. Soon he began to rethink beauty was not aesthetic but transcendent in its relief. The Jester came to visit him still, until the prince realized he was a figment of his imagination but now that he was a definite illusion, real happiness came. He lived his days in the tower slowly resting on the simple gardens. (There was the desire to own the word "argument," guarding its semantics safely. It was possible that if true progress continued, suffering would accumulate more meaning).

Beauty became a red stain on a white table cloth and surfaces were trust-able in their complexity.

A FEW YEARS LATER: Date a Year from Previous Poems: Poems from a Future Journal: The Following Dream Once Bewildered Me: Surface

Jenna had a dream in which some major player on the world's scene comes to Winnipeg. She reported it as simply as would Betty, who was with us also. I will describe it simply. Instead of a red carpet, a giant band-aid is rolled out. The major player is taken aback by it but makes a witty statement, that, alas, Jenna cannot remember. It makes everyone think of *band-aid solutions*. Having—ironically—no other place to go, the figure steps on the band-aid. At that instant, a clearly painful yell emerges, belonging to a poor sick person, as everyone in the dream understands with standard dream knowledge of what you couldn't know in waking life. The figure steps to another part and hears another cry, slightly different on a now-absurd musical scale. To make it seemed planned, the figure begins to play a song on it, the mayor joining in, dancing from part to part. This is very much related to the story of mental illness in all cities except a city of madness as I will show later. Imagine if a cut grew a band-aid itself.

Disclaimer by Colin Verbanofsky This poem might not have been possible without the illness *and* recovery.

The Author Recognizes Language as Representing Surface as
Strata

On the surface, everything seemed *fine*, like the end
of a French play. But you can't make a grave
of every instant, even on a mirror's surface, which pretends to have
depth. Hollywood now remodels the universe
while the person next to you
thinks past the psychiatrist couch's shadow
to the nearest possible escapist vacation though they can't get past it.
Disfiguring rain could pop the marble cartoon bubble
of thought that represents an outsider's parody of mental illness.
A devil'd-egg-head advocate's troubling question emerges:
"Should we stay hidden in the displaced forever?"
Amid a marathon of poses in this coffee house where the
archaeologist considers the spoon and digs it.
The streets outside are a coffin that buried nature.

Outside the window you saw a few simple words
life's hieroglyphs of fading dimension
leave themselves for autumn study, and from the page elastic
little hieroglyphs off to school to learn fine print
amid the specimens of everything but disease.
Philosophic *property* is technical music with an ivory ring.
Accept poetry as a toy here of futurity,
a kaleidoscope of cutting edges, vectors seeing Oppenheimer
on the other side of time, wishing he had built the atom.
His mind also as divided as confusion,
a word that stood for itself gives birth to its de/re-constructor,
what might we call words that change themselves,
those little hieroglyphs
putting on Socratic school uniforms? Our new senses
of the old words: schizophrenia splits a voice, a powerful word:

synonyms, retronyms or victims of etymology,
not just any old words growing old.

The anthropologist sees surface in a museum and does not the
noble dinosaur force kids to pull-away softening cartoon flesh?
You can refute metaphysics by kicking a stone (proof-rock universe)
watch with jealousy how animatedly it skips up the path, free
like the proletariat princess's pea, into a bleak field that vagueness
    refines with mist.
If *preciseness* could *dawn*…
The times, in varying degrees of literalness and actuality, are in mist.
And here, with steaming cappuccino you are trying to modernize
with society a cup of tea, everyone in the room
at a respectable distance.

Heroic couplets would be a stretch if you thought a pearl lay under
a mattress repeated according to some form of disciplinary meter
that now in the poems' order I decide to render as an issue sundered.

You are here and they are there; a railroad in your spine reminds you
there are tunnels in the air leading to portraits.
To listen to the sound of the clock's statement, for our future,
    the conjunction clock says "and" but soon says "therefore."

The last century: most of the old objects are not working:
Nietzsche did not ever hold a hammer,
the pillar of a smoke factory pretends to hold up the sky.
           And so, while I am
nailing the categorical imperative to the outhouse open to all or one
is it possible that there is an imagination of the diseased imagination?
Like a children's book about paranoia that makes it sound fun?
Anyone can enter our illness, a fact, that by the world, is shunned.
Can I make them judge me with hammers as gentle as a piano's?

Should I try to melt a compass along with the clock?
No. There is a compass that grew here and that I need.
Schizophrenia. I thought about this word again as if it just
meant "diagnosis" and was unable to hold back a laugh.
A real laugh that
was not violently defiant, as if to deny that I would be the reverse of
that character I once read of in another text
who looked around to see how others acted, and thus
was seen as what
not to imitate. I tried to imagine a human voice saying it with a
    humane tone,
but realized I was in public. *Mental illness* is ingenious
as if behind its literalness is an Oz for zombies, as Rick might
    appreciate. The other word,
Schizophrenia, is another matter altogether.
Some think that we are simply a radio
unable to find the obvious song/ and I hoped to get past the
        rhythm in the static there all along.

Memory: A Poem that Deals with
One's Personal History of Illness
And a Consolation

You were just trying on those cement shoes of reality
ready to dip into the sweat of an honest day. A glance skyward
pierces the deluded clouds with keen and refreshing heroism:
the mind's drift, the burrs of punctuation weigh. But,

You carry, with dignity, a strange burden through
the broken parade of slight individuality; the Hollywood-
Goodbye-people of Alka-Seltzer smiles wave in mirages.

But do you find yourself, or who you were?
Causing quite a caustic stir.
Vultures in the mind (or on the brain), is that you?
In a nest of chalk, an aura of weak stone draining hue?
            As if on the weather channel:

"Local streets are possessed by ghosts and some occasional wind
thoughts of hell should be moving in to deal with this. O clouds!"
We can make an ode of all this, a submission of eventual
stillness instilled with an angel's strength; the street will stop
with you, when you do, like the fantasy of a sculptor.
            The traffic will be a thousand and
one coffins carrying your exhaust away/ wind your pallbearer.

You never forget when sickness sent its vultures
you were a kid playing with a cornucopia filled with marbles
that are all gone as you stand before the playground
trying to translate the children's laughter and yet how effortlessly
tragedy and comedy,
unwilling to speak with you, push you back into the crowds.
Walk above the river and look down and you will remember:

suicide leaps up at you.
It might seem like a puppy dog, its eyes drooping like a sad dream.
Its face the you you wouldn't be/ a baby face/ you pick yourself up.
A path between people opens.

End of Reflective Later Poems
The Text Now Returns to Where We Left Off in Time
We Find Ourselves/ Suffering Retreats

I woke in the middle of the night and waited for any voice,
a game show of voices perhaps, as I thought of all the doors. "…
There is a pregnant moon tonight…" the phrase hung like a mobile. I
yearned for private symbols that would not be explicitly symbols.

With a "pregnant moon" enigmatically unresolved
(could be full or crescent), then dissolved
suddenly into careening, streaking stars
that no matter what you say they are
their being, through metaphor, refuses to be stalled."

Yes, to *exhaust* moonlight so *it* can dream a new self!
Marinetti had a plot to kill the moonlight but who is that perversely
dedicated?! Evacuate the lovers! Neil Armstrong could not be
reached for expert commentary! Give the children black paper and
ask them to draw their family: maybe the father works a night shift!
Will the man on the moon wink, just once, for the people?

Pledge

Edit away, like a controlled avalanche,
the pale blanket under which you cocoon nightly
                as if peeled from fake moonlight.
You step out and see no sun,
only neon veins as perplexed as a robot's red-wire sexuality.
Nor do you hear the sentinel rooster on its usual postmodern
cliché: its call to dawn, infinitely quotable,
through energy. Instead it gives a dawning of pure
sound, and all it tells us is that we should be
listening more carefully. If the walls had
ears there'd be wax brown wallpaper colour unanimously,
                across creation.
We, with calloused osmosis wonder
why this sound should tell us
what to do when the condition of music asks so much?

The voice then says that evidence a) is what we seemed not
to notice when an indulgent bird ate the sun (speaking now)
and excreted the moon which numbly sang to tentative oceans.
Only one person volunteers to see what will happen
to the moon when it is part of a great crash scene in the sky
with headlight stars and little bonsai machines
                toyed in distances.

"An artist will make it to the moon before the next
Beat Generation craze; in the very beatnik of time!"
Moon be awake! Even in the curdled milk of cosmos
is an inherent lunacy there?
Or is it really no more than blankness registered by outsiders?"

If we had a prairie-Canadian visual artist on the moon (if we acknowledged the mad in our society; how could our grandness be *empty*?) he/she would be very nervous as he/she muttered something about "a mild step, or something," and barely move, as if waiting for Godot. The degree of open space would have brought him/her back to our history of huge openness that we do not spatially allow as dense, rich storage that lets in our language. Will our flags always be at half-mast compared to America's where the eagle jet-planes, striping the stars? Yet Canadian metaphysical history is not to be confused with American creationism. "This is a big step for me personally... though where I come from it really is not... I am from the prairies, the uncreated empire fighting the history of wind. I would also like to report that I don't see any serious insanity here, on this moon. All the same, since we got here in *reasonable* time, planting this flag could wait. We are the inside-outsiders of prairie."

Conversational Overture: Dr. Earwinker and Colin Having to Split

Colin: "It is very possible that I do not have schizophrenia, but that I tried to hide the idea of void with voices. In human misery's echo, this is a soundtrack out."

Earwinker: "But then a real schizophrenic might say that you have covered 'noise' with 'voice.'"

"Yes, but I am looking for a fluke, for schizophrenic admittance that somehow a mythic image from the unconscious will reveal a path that explains why this mess of mind happens. The mind should be our master-piece, and if it is receptive."

"But are you suggesting that 'voice' is the proper way to get there, to this explanation?"

"Yes. I hear patients mumbling to themselves, and it is my way of not seeing it as wasted energy, like encyclopedias of minute-sized scribbles."

"That's a mere sentiment. We need to be realistic. Loss has its own urgency."

"I am beginning to think that the mind is increasingly rhizomatic in madness. I find in myself a singular effect, that I can better relate to human beings with this principle of any point connecting to any point. In my view, it is in mania that this multi-connective-ness becomes explicit and that during depression the connections are infused with the shocking weight of their potential totality, making the possibility of ideas being reconnected less likely. Like having a million roads all at once on a moon unlike ours, with severe gravity. My original Critique of Creativity was made during this depression and its effects."

"But if the insane mind is rhizomatic, then there is only a clear model of random chaos. You are still stuck. Maybe more so because of a lack of other possible models."

"But it is perhaps compelling because it has so much dimension, and for me it suggests voices coming from all over the place: an underground polyphony, a conductor's baton gone amuck under the dirt of our realism. Yet I can't help thinking that there is a right order in following it, even though that is so contradictory."

Doctor Earwinker thought for a moment, and said: "As an image it suggests awareness of an unconscious that suddenly shoots up a thought. For the upper part of the model, any point not known to it could be rhizomatic by assumption. I know of a place you must go; it is where the points are almost the same. It is a safer rhizome. We have a new facility that is a kind of solitude experiment for would-be artists, about 50 miles out of Winnipeg. The generic nature of prairie should keep you safe… somewhere where your voice can be separated from those here. You have spoken to the nurse about a Cartesian interruption and this could also be a test to see if you have schizophrenia or not, by helping you escape a kind of anxiety about the influence of the voices around you, which you are so involved with. You need, my dear Verbanofsky, to split from this joint."

"But that is where I lacked any frame…" I spoke quickly, thinking of an instance with the wind with a sense of horror.

"To let your own voice absorb and digest influences, this will perhaps be the place where you can go to allow your voice to become truly yours." He reflected for a moment and then said, "I hope you don't find this terrible, but the idea of a voice being able to build a hospital might be quite interesting to see. Your voice might yet prove to be a kind of dome over the heads of your people as you protect them along with the way sometimes a purging occurred when a person who embodied madness in a particular way was sent away, in the history of mental disorders. We can see how they perhaps experience catharsis." I noted his mention of my people with its air of possibility. A pause not quite Proustian spurred the question:

"So why haven't I heard about this place?"

"Because it is modelled on the unconscious."

A Bridge across Time/ Winding like a River

—Sky is—
    feather ending/ exhausting/ slowly bending
land   collecting desperate objects: an
      architecture of catch me!
    if you
canned is
  a suicidal form of building
a Canadian barn with a
 sagging roof   a new form if a tessellation aloof
  all exoskeleton of fading style to be less
and less reliable than a street sign.
Banality might be numbed by snow.
    It is the inability to make a roof to match
    nature's sky/
flat bombast barely buoyant car's wheel a cog turning in the head.
You see, because of the non-existence of
   history here, no tourist would believe
     us
to be   more than a few minutes old over all-time.
Insanity is ancient,
our history is a tedious weather report we consort with
    speed on the highways
       old yellow sun/ undulating
         and we are facade-makers of smiles to
    tourists who think
  the style of the roof-decayed barn
must be an *intentional architectural bow*
  to Frank Lloyd Wright or
    whatever the pillar does not "stand for,"
 because there is not enough time here for a building to
decay like that.
    They think we are just suburbs without centres.

Are we creatures of
                        geographical destiny
where and when Sisyphus had it easy,
kicking stones into ditched rhizomes?
        All the fairy tales of future and Heaven with modest lure
        here madness can be as large as anywhere else
        though no one looking at us gave us our own need
for paranoia.   This endless afternoon
                dutifully and yet buoyantly sponsored
by a gentle suggestion of where the wind might have gone.
A little church keen against clouds (objects don't work in this space)
        might suffer the same fate as the barn. O dome
that could have been
                would have sealed our bleeding minds.
        In this little car, seeing this ubiquity I have repressed
                as my window is up, like a church's, stained with bugs.

I watched the prairie go by thinking of Kroetsch's absences. If we
went by the Manitoba desert we'd say "this is where the pyramid
should have been."

New Section
Journal Entry: First Day at Institution

        My room shows a spatial mastery that one might expect
from a custom-fitted art-space: bar-less windows, the ornate bed
a rhetorical structure built by some ancient arcane dreamer who
performed a medical Humpty-Dumpty miracle when the egg tried
to bounce off the walls that are not as soft as they say. The view
outside was no less beautiful than its inner comfort; I could see a
beautiful stream that disappeared like a truant, around the corner
of the woods. There is evidently a lake nearby as well. The room was

on the third story of what looked on the outside like a barn and an old monastery. There was, I discovered, a kind of arcade, that was entirely good decorum for the prairies, and a courtyard in a low-laying *part* of the building. It consisted of only a single story, which made me think that I could look things straight in the eye. I was reminded that I was in a particular place, which seemed necessary in my illness. It did not happen in an attic in Europe. There were also scaffolds that suggested the building was still in development, which it took me a while to realize was actually a good thing! An admittance that it was still being developed, similar to a confession, I suppose, and I was also told by the doctors that there would be a basement that was a fallen sky-scraper.

Horizontal Tales—Prairie Spacial

But soon I wanted to imagine a vision of Winnipeg's re-formation, like mushrooms after hail: (a small town affected by big city lust in ruined stillness)—this great open road beggared by road-side detractions while back home our violence on the street with graffiti semiotics is possessed by real insanity, a nihilism of why not? applied with blatant viciousness to Jackson Pollocks on the flesh: emblematically, there is a propaganda talk, a technocracy of the knife twisted like good fiction and a notion of a re-colonization of the streets… but out here that is all impossible, undesirable.

You could just barely fantasize there was a city here with pedestrian highways
We have a sphinx face in fields/ flinching at simplistic tourist Q and A's.

(Our city's horizontal rush could almost invade/ there would be a ruin of these faint traces of place). What of stillness's architecture

that is the city in stasis, brick rock gardens, river suicide-slit sewage
pipes while, like a minimalist economy, dust is passing up web
in evaporating dew spied in some fade of nature—the garden is
precisely unruly but tame as the garter?

Digression's dams for wind tunnels weave/ not in Canada anymore
"portage and main" a comparative satiric refrain we vainly believe (a
train passes through this through-line like a skeletal narrative).

To have relatively recent historical stall/ a bouquet of stop signs for
the golden boy whose silence calls to me (and would be a model).
What of a relatively new city with an interest in nostalgia and a
natural history museum?! like a constructed spill in memory?!
Buildings that are less than huts, holding timid capitalist clingings to
roads, flippant dreams of shop windows' poor concealment.
                    And, a weak Whitmanic celebration of sameness.
      Like a doorbell to an empty suburban house
—democratic ring in unofficial cages.

In these fields I felt like a discoverer—not a colonizer—the latter who
reaches down and picks up a hunk of clay, and with some incipient
villainy, smiles, and thinks of moulds and absurd ego boundaries;
but more as the farmer reaching into the soil and thinks of roots
breaking moulds with sudden vegetable able-ness I thought I would
dream of the city tonight; perhaps it would be a lucid dream a
welcome mat of huge houses the quaint parade to drag history into
our docile scenery of an almost credible day in history.

The bricks of the road to hell were used to make its walls, yes/ but out
in agoraphobia, the nightmare horses of instruction meet the horse
power of the mouse cats of wrath/ the mole of spying judges both
as over-reactions: it is the stealth crow of precision who decides.
Bursting wine bubbles he rises from the dead magpie (beyond,

in our city's night life) like Dionysus. Smaller visions of power
are ours despite industrial-strength cologne of smoky incensed
flowers. Pointillist light points to a historical re-imagining of nature
made simpler by ecosystems but in acid rain storms things are not
annointedly kissed. All these animals are needed to re-build the city/
on a palimpsest of welcome mats.

If you are in distance long enough it causes yearning /the first seed
of heaven the flower of Nirvana the gulp in the purgatory of the
stem—and these fields: all stems get a root's funeral here/ sinking like
unconscious fingers, prodding subtlety into the ambivalent soil /the
rounded Renaissance person finds a flat foil:
of place <u>verses</u> space.

If I were distance I would be from a spilled cup
an object known for space/ being escaped from
objectification is a pun that relies on special grasp
I scoop up clay/soil with a cup and make a small trench around
myself.
How will we use space when borders become used for hiding?
The city without memory made from moon meteors is our
otherworldly ivory re-rising
a near world: in the complacent comfort zone is forged
a rocking chair for coping at the fear of moving—an object seemingly
gorged
on the poorly-conceived prairie porches
like Wordsworth's definition for poetry our interiors are huge for
emotional over-flow
this inside is the intangible rub: solved and represented by our seed-
crossed soul.

Choosing Another Private Symbol for Madness: The Reeling
Moon No Longer Stars
The Bonsai Rhizome of the Roots: A Seemingly Random
Object: Also Prairie Object

And so the moon lost its sway; overweight star, steady, not so fast…

Imagine instead an object getting less and less itself—instead of the
mind that super-condenses "no ideas but in things" said a doctor,
distantly…
                    "Objects are closer
            than they appear" to disappear into our memories and
    watercolour thoughts from which the slight abstraction
    of the mythic
    object begins as things "are symbols of themselves" which
                makes no sense unless you listen to the doctor.
            You start with the object and you take its representation
    to use it and when you return
    to the object, it is a "symbol of itself." It has an idea
                    of itself; and if they go through stages they can
    be more dense symbols than before…
            "Selves" refers also to the human projecting we do/
    this happens in sickness too.
                    The object in the mirror asks the
    same thing; the self possesses an object awareness.
        Am I now the chosen symbol for what I was
            by what I was? The faulty rear view mirror miniaturizes
                so much. The moon in confused tragedy tugs me
    out by the roots,
        as it drifts to dreams in another more silk space-time fabric.
    How to represent the moon's trace?
    A historical noology.
                If I go to the fairy tale mirror of mist/
            my face be pock-marked?

"You are the only man on the moon."
It lies in perfect stone/ phenomen-ill-logical
       object in the darkness you
could almost hold onto it,
relatively speaking.

Funny Thing Happened on Way to the Hospital: The Vision
That Occurred/
Colin Recounts with Visiting Dr. Earwinker Considering the
Mad Vision that Caused Him to Go into the Dark Night and
Enter the Suggestive Narrative of this Poem

      "… Then I began to get a quickening of a vision…the sense
of time became so fast people were in a history class, it seemed,
and there was an educational film playing and an announcer's voice
was suggesting that the invention of every new automatic weapon
began a new age, a mockery of time considering the bronze age and
the stone age, say. Bullets are launched into space to make futurist
arguments and in fossils we find corporate logos. People trying to
say something beautiful and unique are deflated, fall hissingly to
flabbiness and robots wired to podiums lecture on life. But then it
made sense somehow. The new guns were subliminal but sensical;
it was simply that, through the power of media, time can be
represented as illusionary, and every new super-weapon can inspire
a whole set of reactions. Bullets sent into space were displacements
to defeat a meteor that might collide with earth. The teleological
implications of finding logos in fossils encourages the idea that
reality "is the way it is" and always has been and always will be…
saddest of all to bring thoughtful beauty into the world: how odes
of logic destroy beauty… a horrible weight-loss program applied to
a pregnant mind. Ahem! By which I mean the intellectual valued as

useless by misapplication. But there was a balance…"

Doctor Earwinker: "Your fear sits at the exact balance of creation and destruction in your sensibility. Above all, logic can be blamed for destruction, like a syllogism drained down to the atom. But that duality is like—" We both, at the same time, blurted out: "A terrible symmetry!" Dazed, I continued, with the vision growing ever stronger.

"What terrified me was that a God that could be exactly mathematical and then absurd meant a new level of connection, a new rhizome, as we would now say, that I had tried to control. As a child, even though I liked books more, I imagined God as a mathematician and, though I was not bad at math, I thought of the Einsteinian levels of physics and this preserved a mystery in relation to God. That is, until my encounter with the wind that made me fall in love with the idea of frames. I discovered God in the wind. God is changing in his vision then; what I always feared, another reason why I became a bureaucrat. I was a secular monk. The idea of God changing was jolting, and paradoxical if it was infinite… how could it change? Now I realize my vision in a time of fundamentalism was a personal one, and belongs to me. The voice asking "can you represent me?" was, I almost decided, the voice of God aware of my memory of that initial experience as a boy but also the night I snapped and it somehow involved the voice of God ringing out to all the possible meanings it could have been including…. I fell in love not originally with frames but with anything that acted as an enclosure which it could be because it is changing in eternity. Yet I felt it was the void speaking, despite how paradoxical that actuality would be in its implications. So, you see, my first night in the hospital, that dream I had, with what I had called the 'Roman Rash—' it was the prairie and the expanding was a strange awareness and my illness was defamiliarization, understood in literary terms of course."

Doctor Earwinker: "What did God say? And why do you describe it as emptiness? Would not God filling space be a divine, so to speak, experience? Could it not be the animation of the prairies in some sense?"

" *'And if one suddenly did take me to his heart: I would perish from his stronger existence.'*"

"So you wonder where to put this category of voice...?"

I blurted suddenly a thought that seemed necessary: "It was merely wish fulfilment; I was a repressed creative person whose mind exploded with psychological longing."

Ontological Poem: Author Un-Certain of Exact Words Spoken
with Deity

 Can you represent me?
On the lamb/ from Bethlehem
      not slouching
in perfect body language in sand pause
   ouch ouching enters our world, which could be defined
         as a Gnostic experiment gone wrong covered up with makeup.
Minds are more static than the birth and death of
         locusts storms/ and a dogma of stuff while go-getter tyranny
            loosens its power to *utter angst* who would not
               harvest decadence even if you personified it.
"Do you really expect me to come out in all of this?"

Betty would have said that to me if we talked about how the Messiah
   returning to the world was like an insulted
      guest seeing a disgusting doormat.
It would be her theological statement.
      (*"Then the voice of God said unto me"*)
(You should not be able to paraphrase God and yet,
how could you not?)

"Do you think I am a ghost of
myself in the machine that I hover
over the theatre of your bad acting? Or a piñata
   of candy apples and I will mend all
problems like the lightning welder of half-human
         will in my impossible compassion?
Why then am I here, you ask? Because I am polytheistic.
Someone with a lion's head and the body of a woman is coming."

"I would scream a (rhetorical) question at you but I am already your performative nightmare." Meanwhile, the wind obeyed serious literary decorum and blew fiercely. Cold, I ran back inside.

The World's Attitude to the "Mad" Wrestled into a Poem Meditations on How the Prairie Is the World with Its Endless Journey Space and Imagining Neighbours: Thinking Also of the Voices of Other Literati: Being Alone/ Are the Voices in Fact a Poor Experiment of Self Sufficiency Because We Must Be "In Praise of Character in the Bleak Inhuman Loneliness?" The Voices Are a Plenum Performance Piece

Two-way cure of the sick: sever worlds with a curtain
drooped like fantasy armour. Censor the thought of Galileo-brand
telescopes staring down voyeurs. Madness is unseen
an obsessive thought or the opposite of love at first sight in the eye...
Film a person writing an elegy "given" by the castle-lurking Gods:
rewind. Modern myth of Sisyphus.

Dreams of leaving deepen/ curiosity dissects blackness.
In the park somewhere children are playing siren
with the vividness of
the innocent known to the prophet Blake. You hear
that crazy people are "characters who like unreliable narration,
conspiracies lost in the details, all heated finely over
too much worry with a small portion of cool nerve salad."
Yet if there could be sight from a gamut,
Blake wrote of the tiger and the lamb.
That the same God made each could be marvelled like a statue
    of a Minotaur, the comedian riddler/ the straight line(s)
making a labyrinth.

But madness is a *tiger in sheep's clothing*: a viscous inside rotting
a removal from actual nature, a thing made of Frankensteins
whose imagination is part of all of them and death seems
a bug-eyed god as you float up you seem torn to pieces until at last
all of yourselves come together as a camera takes over (movie
image who is watching Sisyphus). But *Catatonia* is the cat as a vessel
of thickening sleep here we invent a word that could almost pass...
The cat sees the universe fall to dreams, in its eye sockets you
could stick the whole world when most of us were in bed.
But the cat somehow has an albatross caught in its jaws.

A gamut...

The shepherd walks from sight and into sense now he overlooks
the crowd at the mall buying wool shirts without memory of him.
The city is mad in its forgetting/ sees a tree, remembers to give
shadows to awareness.

And a winding route with its branches
pointed the experiential way/ heaven-headed

disarray—

> *Forced* to take the road less travelled by
> we negotiate endless differences.
> In a time when the freak should rule
> we agree certainly over dissonances.
> Is a dropped hammer a master's tool?

But any failure of judgement that would be useful,
    I sense in my mind
that the voices are becoming people. What is language? A sculptor
    that gives us
hands incapable of grasp, arms a little too large in proportion?

Only the wind.

Colin Stares at the Ceiling: Science/ Art Model Vertical or Horizontal

Dear Reader: hold page so that it is vertical facing you like a wall.

As a Video Game of *Tetris* at First: These Stanzas Collapse
Dramatically and
Might Enable a Game of *Scrabble* when All the Words Fall to
Pieces: (Do My Ideas Come from God?)

> Grandeur is a form of opened emptiness Jack
> where the haunted echoes say "it ain't so."
> You are verbally posing Sistine Godly-esque
> reaching to a mirror, envisioning no below.

Milton You didn't make friends with the Sistine graffiti floor.
A wing-wounded realist, you would abhor
making a fantasy knowing how depressed feeling
looks at the walls and almost never the Platonic ceiling.

Earwinker Dashing hieroglyph hyphen of the disciplines,
you felt the lynch of near omniscience
over the ornate confusion since
barrenness birthed exploring implosive wings.

> Indistinguishable tragic comic mask/querading Rick
> as a face; synaptical conjunctions parading
> like a spine you cannot trace into conspiracy, near,
> the words you appropriate have agendas unclear.

Vorseth Either pillar or Falstaff: anti-hero laugh
at existence for taking gravity seriously.
When you confuse epigram with epitaph
as I will now, you sleep almost fearlessly.

Under your arched eye; nemesis-genesis.   Roary
The civilized yawp from the soap box opera
you denote sounding pleasant to end this
Mozart-esque silence that who is the author of?

Etymology would chase music if progress   Sal
was not a delusional rhetorical embellishment
to x-ray through all words as if cautious
to express the genesis note of muse-development.

Like the earth's there is an atmosphere for everything   Jenna
you see; on your way to touch *braille*, a description:
Your epiphany of air as successive readings.
A little dot of acne can actually say "blossoming."

Nurse Vella Omniscient over the strange emotions,
            voice of reason that echoes and a use of light
        neither innocence's nor experience's nor intuition's
        that combines all these like a tangible feeling, in sight.

      Betty   Tossed Rock Boyfriend
With an inner child mantra-ing "womb"   "Her heart was a locket
you hide behind the erosion of a bonsai wall. that melded closed
Your queried mind paradoxically loomed   your tool shed.
over a toy atom of inevitable sprawl.   Your heart was a
                                              pocket that
                                              unfolded into a bed."

Allison The endless imagist odyssey of your face
          drifts into my futurity; the past cranes its birth
          back and I the egghead, lay my mirth
          upon your universe's chalice: such inner space!

(Here with all I can read I utter ambient descriptions and
          defamiliarization fresheners).
          "Granted, it is altogether true
          that we must believe in God's
          existence because it is taught
          in the Holy scriptures, and
          conversely, that we must be
          lieve in the Holy scriptures
      because they have come from God."
      — Rene Descartes, *Meditations*

Circular argument; sphere of (Colin   ) philosophy could also call
satellite notes/ A square consists of straight lines pretending to be a
                          circle.

*Now, reader, place this poem down on a preferably flat surface, and
imagine that the falling thought of your initial reading has now become
a solar system with I, Verbanofsky, as a temporary centre. In a sense
now, you are with me in my room, where I have conjured the voices to
almost become full-fledged phantoms, and you can see what it is I have
done. I have managed to keep the voices distinct, and if you read this
passage quickly, perhaps we could imagine these stanzas more as snow
flakes, ideal for the analogy of child-like idiosyncrasy. This uniqueness
is very apparent now, but earlier, it was my attempts to keep the voices
distinct, as if some composite thing far more complex than the most
complex Minotaur of the most complex labyrinth, that kept me sane.
You can also, dear reader, hold the poem over your head and imagine
it as a Sistine Chapel in which humanism is indicated through the*

mutability in each description of the character's stanzas (I wrote them quickly), while it is also a vision of science, and my loneliness now has cast them as planets. It is here that my emotions get in my way, for I kept Allison and Betty closest and I put Roary at a numerical centre so that you see I am offering myself as one possible centre, her as another. Jack with his—at times—God-like arrogance is how I would imagine the highest point of the Sistine image were it a round dome except that he is also there because his singular and glib voice is what I will consider mad—based on the very first thing he said to me, that all voices were derivative of his. All voices, it seems to me, are composite both in relation to discourse and the fact that every voice is, in a different sense than Jack suggested, composed of other individual and impossibly nuanced voices. Where he is placed, he can simply drift away into a scientific universe since his stanza mentions not looking down and Milton, below him, is isolated, as I imagine is his fate, also cut off, partially because I dislike him so much. They are all rotating in my mind as we were all in little rooms like the one you just made with this page, moving it about and you sense, perhaps, a universe contained in a small room.

Colin Takes On a Written Project with Others from Back at the Health Sciences:
Post Card Problem
While reading Proteus chapter of least narrative frames in Book One of Ulysses.

I am trying to describe a huge lake. Signifier/signified: in the sign a great more than molecular divide. The latter pulls me back since I have just barely mastered it in a tentative second, but the word turns to water (precisely what the lake is)—whose nature is not to be art—but it can't say that verbatim. There is a Braille *The Da Vinci Code* of the miscellaneous stones on the beach, the waves are a verb that ate them, and slowly, it speaks only onomatopoeia, which I theorize is baby talk directed at me because I have not become part of this Protean sway, seizing the sheer power of movement through stony centuries. It washes at the random stone text like a implied reader of Braille, in the milky-white sand you would take a child to if you were to introduce him/her to heaven.

I have tried to represent my madness so clearly that it seems like it was solved. It almost seems to me that schizophrenia is something we invented, not something chemical-biological. I say this despite the danger of this idea and what it might do to us. Only postmodernism could conceive it as a normal condition! It is born of the fall of mania in the constructed psychosis of modernism, that lands us in broken glass.

I challenge you guys to do this with the city. What I just did with nature, I mean to represent it accurately but aware of the signified and signifier. Puns or portmanteaus may seem inevitable.

Reply to Colin Verbanofsky
Near Box 101, Manitoba Prairie
RU2 SO4

Dear Colin: How Do We Poetically Represent these Underlined Ideas as Poems?

From Jenna...
—A great abstract painter forced to paint his deterioration while people he admires watch, but who were advocates of his abstract mode.

Colin: As a poem, heroic couplets fall into an elegy of loss too complex to understand. So, the poem is brief to hide this. How does one compose oneself here? Perhaps a concrete poem, with the pen saying 'erosion' acrostically as words spill. A ballad about free verse with an ode to time itself?

From Vorseth...
—Possible poem based on a day dream. I ran wild like the river over its rapids, reaching ever more with these beautiful spires of purple flowers everywhere. Then the sudden nudge in class because I was speaking aloud; *those are purple loosestrifes, they are murderous."*

Colin: This war of biology deserves a pastoral of a black sheep that is written in the dark. Also an epiphany, perhaps a careful reflection of odes. You must be careful to consider decorum. In that consideration, add *The Flowers of Evil* in a concession. You could also have an imagist poem about something rotting beautifully, whether being the nightmare above the dying flower bed or the chemicals that finally kill this murderous flower. Experiment also with "In A Station of the Metro" and the colour mentioned. Nice to see you have begun to move in your imagination.

Lyrical Diagnosis

At a certain point... the arbitrariness
between word and thing brings the hammer of
judgement, shatters the sound
barrier's hush to all but wit and of my fledgling
from my egg monolith:
dreamers brought me back!
The alien universe cracked/ bleeding black.
You have to believe in language
that a heart monitor is not
                a crack or a machine immune to metaphor.
A burlesque universe where you need
maps to the next room, you are a physicist of dust.
All of this was simply the feeling of bombast
to a/void being a speck of mythic self
you made your tears a telescope.
But you learn that instead of displacing you
find instead the stronger-good rather than less-bad.

A little bib of bile melancholia from a nervously bitten pen
is this poem's plenum blanket, now a sterile language
a *momento mori* of feeling itself and of anguish
painting as if the oil sky were watercolour bleeding
becoming utterly numb.

I leave the idea of my diagnosis on the street: senseless thing.
I let strange energies fight over it. In a warm-looking house,
I see wax rushes down a candle,
in prose, it means nothing perhaps... just the data of love collapsing/
                the weight of statistics.
Who blinks at chivalry surprised to hear the word?
A pizza delivery guy arrives roughly on time.

I keep walking no more than
a ghost through walls that aren't as calloused as people.
I am perceived only by doctors and the acutely sensitive.
A poetic line can attack me at any time
in the middle of the street's crossroads as if
Dante might lead me through the alleys
where those who abused language are forced
to talk only about garbage in advertisements. They sit
in the high burlesque air avoiding stench,
posing like Rodin's "The Thinker" on a toilet
installed by Marcel Duchamp, told only the ends of poems.
Vowels stuffed with consonants… like Vorseth's mind.

My head is made of split wounds giving birth
an open mouth begging for healing.
Our condemning labels preserve my alleged catatonia
like an Egyptian mummy.
       I do not believe in a physical heart/
       that beating you hear is in my gut.
       The snake ate the apple and spoke for and against it.
An eraser is the anti-defamiliarizer; it absorbs us as
streams of Lethe do, like an exhaust pipe of pan the eraser
could be the heart erasing itself to find/
       the first thought of the heart by the mind.
It was an object as paradoxical as a dreaming human
in a material age, a kind of irony and almost a soul.

As His Name Does Indicate: You Might Have Been Expecting
This: Yawp: A Monologic Frame
"So I guess you have all us basket-cases in a single egg, do you?" Rick
asked me this in a letter.

"Our suffering is a marionette with strings for every tear.
A mobile universe insinuated, a sagging malaise prone to fear.
To find metonymy in the vernacular, we are "reduced to tears."
Yet we are a divided body, thanks to Descartes and iambs;
One to involve poetry and "the questioning air of philosophy."
The slaughtering of clouds so like the learning of lambs;
A piercing of sunlight and a new pillar somehow stands
you might imagine an apple there, our spines a calloused tree."

A New Critique of Creativity: Hide His Bureaucrat Identity/
Faintly

The idea I would like to criticize is not that art is too much; it is
that life is too little. Still, the voice of creativity is too clever to ever
compress the world, bursting at its seams, into some Einsteinian
"formula." In madness it might be: *The Elegy Epiphany for Existential
Gain.* But *cold* formulas, like a distant professor, rarely discuss their
coldness. Saussure re-invented semiotics, a science of words. He
semiotically exposed the chasm. Would his commemorative statue
balance on the proverbial fence, tottering between words and things
with interiors? Perhaps there are poems which affect reality as do the
great realizations of physicists. I guess that $E=MC^2$ is actually quite
beautiful. Yet a line that I love signified something else: "there are
still songs to sing beyond humankind." And I can picture William
Blake, caught up in visionary chase-scenes with energy itself, and
representation no longer rolled in a nutshell. If we, too, could do so,
perhaps we might think of all things as alive with metaphor. And I

was the bureaucrat who almost did not put his name down beneath his work, and I would settle my name, in a surprise, *on* and not *by* the *x* of *sous rature* where my bureaucrat identity would be not rid of but re-thought on an imaginary cheque. I would sign my name a new way and add: "thread suns… a high thought strikes the light tone." This grazes grace and suggests that Genesis could be written as if distilled, through a pen hooked up to the universe.

The Author of a Scream (More Dialogic) Polyphonic Yawp Removal of Periods

1.
The mind of unity cracks us/ like gradual lightning in glass
                         thinking… the only clarity
was following the sharding itself, edge as a sculptor would like it
Huddled like nerves, cold, waiting upon non-sequitur leaps,
                         languished in limbos
we are forever between judgements with our sincere confusion,
weaving tentative synapse, holding ambiguous hammers
In an instant we are lost in the small shadows of the "healthy," those
                         mannequins of marrow
We are not enamoured in the ideological store fronts of consumer
                         bot reality
We pass like *things-in-themselves* with an explanatory carapace leak,
     snails to our own private life's too-apparent confession breech
reflective like a Socratic dialogue about immediacy/ a fractal
                         moment in the monumental
Because "what you feel will find its own form,"
what you were hiding counts
Our language is the adjective caught in the mime's life, we seem
                         inexplicably trapped
with numbness and its hibernation under the skin resulting from a

lynched world

of dreams and the presence of a monster in the crown of swollen
conscience

with eyeball abacuses of what's-the-point? Strewn former patches in
the wallet,

of your flat smiles endless like a gut crudely extracted from a clown's
body, an inward

monster's face is a perfectly articulate lion posing as the emblem for
angst's jowled yawn

as we try and catch scraps

The monster's crime scene is too hot and then cold for elegy

Shadows of children going to learn far too much, too quickly, reels by
as you sit

like a king or queen of decadence in an otherwise stalled universe

The smallest shadow is trampled… the children *play* in the
nightmare;

you see their lunch-pails and register baggage

And so we dream a self impossible, because we know that time will
eat us in the

hour-glass and so what is the symbol strong enough for preventing
this diffusion of time?

It is ourselves *creatively declared* in the fertile cutting floor of myth

With our imaginations fully intact we declare ourselves of the Braille
text read by erosion's index finger/ the more eroded a part of us is
the more a new one emerges

like the overweight hallmark texts that water a vegetative heart with
excess chicken broth

we forge descriptions of mountains that we climb everyday/ flames
on the moth

2. A Personal Cry to Cure through Realizing the Story of Individual Delusion
This Part Connects to the Poem of the Stanzas with Colin at the Centre/ About Allison and Betty Here Respectively

You endure as an inventor of things that shows such profundity, with imagination that looks over a seed with every molecular angle of the plant reaching for the sun. One day you will be able to see the clouds in your mind as shaped a particular way, just as an inukshuk made of your everywhere-pointing shoes indicates your pilgrim's run. Your mind gives distilled details to the creative without any foolish hype, and at the piano of existence you would not abuse using the trope of "type" to describe a human being or anything mechanical in a blushing life.

Thrillers whose periodic sentences end with "Boo" are generally meant for children, though immature readers seem eternal in their reservoirs of youth. Who knows what adults pretending to be ghosts hide under a white table cloth by the in-the-dark shadows of boys and girls? The child's imagination runs far from home as sometimes a flower too fully unfurls. There will always be many homes and the world becomes populated by friends so the occasional horror film ends and is chosen by others to make you stronger, better able to play a new adult in panic situations instead of only playing a mother to a child-self any longer.

3. Upon the Realization: Moment in Monumental and Trusting Judgement

"Delusion" is a sign that is a blur in essence but the blur is in all accuracy a signifier that has an uncertain streak of the signified.

Suddenly a flash strikes you; you follow a dove's fluttering legion, those white flags of peace's possible sculpture models and see a perfect brain shape in the clouds and you achieve an epiphany knowing that it is not vernacular blown-smoke and you have a realization there is a vividness in what can be grace. But your mind is real and the world is real, sustained by pillars and she can read the dew of some flower—not to be confused with Blake's sun flower's helio-eccentricity—as an augury of willed innocence insists it knows what that flower, to us, means being a visual thing ringing with Heideggerian buzz and it tells you its name in its own language, a hieroglyph that means *you cannot understand me but only look and yet the dew is like a new language or illustration, a small anti microscope.* You sense an interpretive path and realize the superhighways of synapses everywhere remind one of new works of art and how they will crack along those very lines and you see the path behind the "Mona Lisa" and dream into it and you see a detail for the first time and sense that every small creative attempt is one less barren molecule for the universe to displace itself and the word is no longer just a thing that complacently knows itself but its sound leans on the psychiatry chair and it relates so cunningly to a tangibility in the mind and yet do not objects seem eternal aliens to contemplation, like art with no audience? And you think that if you never lived in a wasteland your footsteps are those of a pilgrim's where everyou are there is a great sleep and the words can get you there. And this is all delusion, as it is not real—but how real is a symbol? Would you interrogate a metaphor in an interrogation room whose soft padded walls helps people imagine our suffering?

You carry your name through life on a shield and the archery of corrector's pens riddle you with arrows and amid language that followed the deformity of thought, you stop, and realize someone is looking at you, and in a dream of fantasy exact, you became a statue for that instant and stand with it as if forever right and true and the sculptor's clouds come and here they pose and run away for eternity.

Dialogue Fragments: On the Purpose of Voice

Earwinker: "You have used appropriation in a way that loses the fundamental condition of your subjects, who at times can barely function. True, decorum in this context is difficult, but you could have focused on their stories. A heart-warming tale of a cooled-down brain, if you will pardon the vernacular, would have been a better way of addressing a public that thinks you all just hear crazy voices. Your implicit voice seems to agree. A story links more to time, there is more room for reflection."

Verbanofsky: "I have also, through this formalization, connected our voices to literature, which in turn could *lead* to better stories for our telling. Besides, would you rather hear the Trojan horse's story from the taxidermist's mouth? Internal life consists of more than a simple narrative. Even in memory, we 'contain multitudes.' All of us do."

Statement: A Giant Inference and Collaboration between a Scientific Mind and Our Hero of Thought: Colin Verbanofsky

The scream reminds the mind of the body, and centres energy in the self and the self un-diffused by certain obligations of language. If we take what is often a popular view—art as expression—then a scream would suffice as art. Now, more complexly we collect pre-thought with post-thought in a way that provokes thought. In a Dadaist perspective a scream against technological civilization would be a natural reaction, one that evokes a theatrical, semantic resonance. It beats the language of bureaucracy, the languages of complacency and political correctness, which direct the scream inward, trapping it as if to form a mouth-less being. To admit that you want to scream shows that you have absorbed much that has made you indignant. But if a scream can be so complex, think of the *thought-process* of those with mental illness, even if we understand how it is thwarted. In the future, a purely phonetic poem will involve a scream into a computer which will blend with your voice's phonetic signature, as an experimental linking of art and psychology. Art is the claustrophobia of agoraphobia, an enclosed openness, a bomb, if you will, of beauty ignited at a simple synapse.

Then: A Confession Outside the psssssst Box: A Letter which Forces Colin to Return
To Visit with Rick

Dear Colin,

    It was I who whispered the line about the "best minds generating, hoowwwl" and I will tell you why I did this. You see, I figured that there was a way in which a set of ideas or statements could become generative enough to preserve qualities inherent in them, in effect creating a living voice, my verbal Frankenstein. Yet I wanted to test it by using the quotes of another, in this case, Allen Ginsberg. It would be, for me, a way of my lasting *through* you, to be the author of some of your thoughts. However, it is perhaps true that what little confidence I had went to you; I actually hoped that you would instil in me a little confidence that I could perceive…
Etc. Rick Genevive.

    After recovering from this confession, I realized how in a mythic sense it was a good thing I focused on all the voices as distinct, else Rick might have usurped my speech, his voice being inventive and comically contagious. I will explain the following poem after you have a chance to read it. In this poem I symbolized *beauty* and he symbolized *humour* which together form a productive coping mechanism that I have realized was central to my survival.

A Collaborative Poem: This Was Written Handed Back
and Forth: Not Spoken/ A Collaboration of Minds Part 1

Rick

Peevish and without experience like a giant
aware of details, the child in its inner-sanctum
at night becomes the host of shadow flags
carried by shadow propagandists, *but mostly shadow toys.*
Conspiracy has crept like an evil clown through a jagged smile.

Colin

The child is used to many things; a window leads
usually to the blue sky where the universe was peeled
away as if it were the glossy skin of an angel
to reveal the ghost.

Rick

The child knows more than that the fridge is where
the cold is kept, that most chairs are friends.
The child experiences wonder before a stain moves its way in.
Who would really know that black is evil's colour? Sin?

Colin

The closet's henchmen refresh horror like a fly
pretending to become a bee. The child senses this
is a door that is to hell what that window is to
heaven and when the imagination
overdoses on a black-hole pill,
all light is reduced to a seed tossed at a bird.

Rick

Yes, the idiot canary slow-dawn into the universe,
the face of this monster belongs to science fiction.
Calloused and starched like an adult,
it deliberately kills audience members during
magic shows. It makes a super-condensed space
where anything could and just might show up.

Both

Never would the child suspect the unlikeliest—
that in the future an adult would form the audience
as the child had previously been.
Thus, through time's mist we came up with the following solution:

Part 2

a)
The adult looked as timid as any lamb
towards the closet that, with wood, he jammed,
and there, within this simple place
was the hiding of more than a startled face.

b)
Inside this place were all sorts of clothes
that could lend to any possible pose.
But, to the person who felt the shadows reel
these were merely a too-soft seal.

c)
For there was a personal monster
whose will could grow ever stronger
when you doubted your own presence
more pronounced grows its essence.

d)
Until you thought people could, in your voice,
sense this rash beast that meant your choice
of what to wear only altered minor things
and that it would mean a hat of a queen or king's

e)

Would remind the kids of the emperor's clothes
that were back in fashion for those who dote
on things unseen. But a too-simple cap
might suggest, in luxury, you took a nap.

f)

And all these problems so firmly set
on that which one would never cast a net
is to say that there is a problem deep within
where monsters can look like anything.

g)

But there is no one to whom you can tell
this malaise combined with a wicked spell,
for if you did, there would be doubt
that you were hypnotized from *without.*

Declaration of Gradual Separation: Meeting of Minds Admits Impediments

The reason we wrote the above poem was because what we
wanted in language was not simply "delusional" so that we could
claim an attempted ownership/ authorship and meet, projected, as
if beaming through mists to not be the kamikaze voices of sonar.
We wrote about the way illness gets hidden in normalcy, but we
displaced the adult's horror by expressing it as a child's and hoped
that our stanza rhyming simulates a logical sensibility to seem more
in control, as a similar technique to my *Dream of Madness/ A Kind of
Strategy.* We needed to write with a kind of framing that will not spill
our thoughts in a vomiting confession.

But you see, I realized what I had done in a much more serious
sense. Take the line: "hypnotized from *without.*" The outside—at

times unimaginative—world produces excellent monsters and so perhaps the idea of madness caused by some internal wilful act, makes a case for greater insanity. If one could *will* such a thing, what contradictory power! If the real voice of God spoke to me, I could have gone mad from *without*. If it was my imagination in an *innocent insanity*, I would by some standards be more mad. However, if the voice of madness spoke to me, in counterpoint with me, was it an independent thing? And if so, perhaps all of my work here has revealed the voice of madness, as an entity in the brain that some are more sensitive to than others. Metanarrative madness was an over-arching voice and it had chosen to speak to me. It is also possible that I failed a test I was meant to fail. If I would say that I could not represent madness, I would never have tried this project of representing it so well as to cure it. A diagnosis is really a first step in a journey that undulates into complexity, as diagnosis is not representational by its nature, whereas the ideas I perceived and sought have been renditions of conditions caused by and around madness. But madness lacked the humanity I discovered in the struggles of those around me, and it is such a shape-shifty thing that naming it is sometimes impossible, so I fluctuate in using terms for it, which gives me a little more freedom. Some times it seemed necessary to attempt to allow madness to describe or name itself. And yet, might I address those who use words like *insanity* with prosaic licence, who think they know this condition? But even the often-used phrase "out of one's mind" is a striking inaccuracy. Because, the very hold that madness can have on one is an inability to step outside it, as through introspection, say, where one is able to judge with a powerful question what one is doing or has done. Luckily, my illness was not like that.

Back at the Health Sciences Centre
In Literary Protest of the Hospital Adopting Yellow Patterned
Wallpaper

The author would like to place the following two poems on a wall
with 1001 other poems of the same size in which these folded mini
pages possess a description of the mad synapse consisting of two
layers. This art piece is dedicated to my conclusion that the writing
on my wall was one subjectivity trying to discover certainty, but not
an absolute of the conditions around madness. The story *The Yellow
Wallpaper* involves a woman who imagines that there is another
woman on the other side of the wallpaper but there is a pattern
that entraps both of them. The two poems directly below break the
pattern of statements as they are about madness in the form of light,
the causal point in my mind beyond even my unconscious. This work
would justify the search; it is my remake of my search for the mad
synapse and possibly the fantasy that there is one. I will leave it on
the wall of either facility as a departure point for discovery for those
who come after me. It also relates all the way back to the Hamlet
readings and the segment *Biographical Note and Critique of Mind.*

Imagistic:

Lemon twist of sun
into drink half full of shit to
care if it is full or not.
The fear is that it should spill
like a fake Jackson Pollock.
Science holding hell fire applauds smoke.
Destruction is hungry: the teeth of ruins,
implosive stomach an obsessive compulsive search.
The mind vomits on a map
full of valleys of go-light-dot distances.
The moon is a frost scar

of abandonment cast away as absolute
reality. Light on a statue's mind
the catatonic hidden in the only reaction
to a nightmare universe of bleeding stars its
eyes see a stone thrown like a tiny shadow
hitting the eye.

Phonetic:

Nietzsche by story light:
Spot the mad synapse bright.
Lightning endoskeleton snake
with insinuation's wormy soul
coils inside the eye, like a corset
string stripping forever
the stability of an absolute slipping
in your shadow maps you endeavour to
match visions in a chess game
between abstract pawns against you.
And even the horses go lame
because death made a deal to
keep madness fresh and real
is its making strange
the most simple tangibles
are out of range and yet there is
a bridge of sheer experience back to the light.

The Final Page of Colin Verbanofsky's Notebook: Returned to Winnipeg Hospital

1.

"Most poets agree to a language for a time." Not: "a poet is slave to political correctness or is faithful to the lyric and never strays from the elegy in the style of Graves and stayed good and loyal to it through eternity." This explains why I blurted out "wish fulfillment" as it relates to a psychological discourse that I intend to fully absorb and use in new ways. My attempt will be to particularize my madness against supposed jargon.

2.

If no God, then the void spoke? The symmetry of the prairie is void and all endless animated sky. We are then the limit of how much void is tolerable, here, these little civilizations on the prairie, this sky that is almost heaven.

3.

Where would you be if *insanity* as a word did not exist, but the experience did? It might be a form of mysticism or parasitic inspiration that loses focus with an inspiration all its own. Is there a word, besides all diagnosis terms, that accounts for the individual's understanding of hiding in a personal logic amid the world that has its own craziness when considered as a whole? For now, lets call this madness.

4.

Perhaps my plan has a flaw, that being the presence of ego I must admit to possessing. If I think I can whimsically transcend it, as ego has gone beyond psychology in the popular thought of our time, I am relating to the re-naming I have suggested in point 1. I ask Roary for the allegorization of my *ego* and *illness*. And with the spirit of poetry you will also transcend into your preferred discourse, should you accept one, likely in the same manner as noted in point 1. A modern allegory would occur simply in moments.

5.

This notebook, this long poem, with some narrative, has been a *Bildungsroman* that became a *Künstlerroman* and yet now a potential theatre script: so much change that this is an index of how much of this work attempts to be a Kunstlerroman. The script could thematically be about anything—perhaps more accurately, its main themes: surface, perception, suffering, existentialism, God, intellect and voice, illness and personification and place/space/locality. Perhaps it is a failed ladder.

6.

On a philosophic level, there is the argument that writing is preferred over speech. But the notebook—and here is its power as a scientific/literary thing—exists between writing and speech—hence its power. It relates to deconstruction thus. Yet I had my speech taken away initially by incoherence. More than a rhetorical artifact is this little notebook.

7.

The dilemma of my God issue was that I did not believe in God just as a madman does not believe he is mad and yet I believe psychologically (but transcending psychology) that what I experienced was God (independent from the fact that I am mad; this was my critique of the divine as the divine connects to my fears about the logical and creative complex that I discussed with Dr. Earwinker). Paradoxically I believe in God now by necessity, and my early *Critique of Creativity* represents my attempt to lessen the power of God so that I could seem creative by comparison; I realize that this is contradictory. I guess I was a conservative and a secret artist simultaneously, but this only occurred in the version I wrote here, and you see I didn't remember what God had said. All the particulars had diffused like a clear sky over a prairie and the dream that was the second entry in this long poem was defamiliarizing for the moment, with its grandeur of madness on the prairie, which is the void mentioned in point 2, which my mind saw as a plenum and had to cover up in some sense. If God was there, it would know where and when in my own mind madness took hold.

8. * see near final pages.

9.

If we combine Foucault's notion that madness signifies the ultimate representational limit, with Wittgenstein's view of language as "the limits of [our] world" (emphasis mine), this suggests we could describe everything from the distance which Milton Phoenix (to give him more credit than he deserves) describes as hell, while accepting his legitimate depression as one of us, an element of our voices.

10.

My diagnosis of Allison is: "Self-Performative Language and Psychosis-Based Imagination." This diagnosis is given with love and she can use the words with the doctors. Tell her it is a new disease as if fresh from the imagination. It was also double take in love (after seeing her out of the group for first time this was my secret diagnosis). She sensed my imagination and believed in it and I, hers; our imaginations fell in love. I know she will come up with a better name for her mind process.

11.

A real pomposity that would suggest I have become the artist I wrote against in the original *Critique of Creativity* is an irony I here perceive; yet Roary's critical voice will edit out what does not work. On this I place my verbal faith.

12.

Dear reader; had you been awake in the ward, you might have heard these voices and created a new disconnection between signifier and signified. And yet, the idea that speech is superior to writing is here "re-versed," as these voices are no longer simply delusions; they are an attempt to become a poem in the broadest sense possible. Because you heard them, or read them, and saw that they made sense, are they any longer simply delusions?

I (Colin Verbanofsky) leave this notebook to be the theatre script of Roary Lionessa and what her outside name will be. She did not have schizophrenia as I suggested in my much earlier note when I asked her what she was thinking when we went a.w.ol. She was referring to our collective voices in our social future as a political, social, and philosophical problem. This begins that voice, and hers I acknowledge to be greater than mine.

The City of Madness/ A City of Light/ An Idea for a City

a)
Pyrotechnocracy was the city-
state model founded by Prometheus
with his "deus formerly mechanical" sensationalist story-light.
This city will never burn to the ground.
It is entirely fireproof, a conceptual
Las Vegas for platonic forms and enlightened zombies.
And a normal idea is the actual sun and in
the triathlon game of the stars it is your moment...
    (((NOW)))

Read with phoney (absolutely certain) voice:

"You've heard of reaching for the stars? Well, what if the stars were all in your head and you were a cartoon? From the makers of What Framed Colin Verbanofsky? comes a story about slowing down the speed of light to experience all life has to throw at you. Coming to a city near you... in the city where you can hide from the sky."

b)
There is
a voice trapped in every voice.
Echoes go to work, etching in egg helmets.
Even the red-light district is a city of semiotic light
though one may prefer
to be safe in warm domestic ambiance that colonizes the night.
          A city confessing its madness,
admitted in the simple semiotic signs: a stop sign graffiti-ed with
"please,"' No U-turn by the museum. You could find a path,
twig allegory of tenuous nature in your pilgrim hand in the park,
          think green lights like good thoughts and keep going.
Freeway ballads involve a little lyric/ honking flourish like de-
winged birds on fat wires moved by electricity.
Meter is not just a tell-tale stomach grumbling
about modern taste ignoring it, but the traffic curses
could be iambic sound-surf.
Fast food restaurants designed like the skeleton of a decadent/ air-
brushed by desert winds,
while the kids play in the sandbox as if miniaturization is
an "index" of control.
You might think of the drama in every small house you pass,
but the mansion is no better, it should be made of crystal
as the future for
theatre and soap operas to the passers-by who see how big
emptiness is.

Insanity is the measuring of a war monument to see if it
represents a statistic's rise in thinking about death
with a column's brow.
In the city, memory possesses criminal statues
with generic faces in go-light beside a huge alley of aesthetic garbage.
Windows made of magnifying glass stretch longing.
What would Blake have thought about meter in the
confession poem about a human admitting the surprise
lyricism of an elegy? To know beautiful people falling
like cats into high heels and thickened soles
balancing somehow like the greed of a corporate tower framing
the sky in a window amid cloud ownership(s).
Through this poem you must understand
that genuine madness is a question your own mind cannot address.
You are outside the space of facts in the philosophy museum
with negative capability. The child's question baffles, aimed accurately
at cosmic mystery like a tell-all-ascope.
Everything hints at the answer, equally, like a movie about
a starring molecule that could be your guide. A
TV ad says, "we are going to a place
where alienation has never gone before: familiarity!"
But the television, to be sellable, must barely care for its location.

The first impression can create a new dimension, like a black hole
that a children's book introduces,
and the TV is a black hole to your life.
We are the radios of longing beyond weather
tuned perfectly to tamed static in an hourglass. We
begin a tragic song whose first notes are capitalist odes, because
you cannot sing of a thing unless you own it!
Next to the oppressive silence of mannequins,
eating a/dress challenging the bull of consumerism.
Someone in a band-aid factory screams

the sun red as if through a horn.
The guardian custodian's mop absorbs its light on the floor beneath
the clock.

And if you stand on a bridge you fall in love with shores.
(Repeat this on every domestic street feeling lost at sea in sprinkling
system's spray).
Poetry is the only language deep enough to fit all the confusion
and give it space. Prose would merely classify a rhizome.
The weather person speaking of the moon in data
is a mute lodged in indescribable music.
If you imagine dying without poetry
you get insanity: you result in or you understand it, or both.
And in this city, you must understand there are those
not officially mad seeking
relief from reason, from the bureaucracies, the wild spinal roller
coaster through boredom's empire.

There are
rooms for madness and there is room for it to brood in colours
one would not expect. Why did the prairie have to be mad,
for me at least?
Perhaps it was the sky, like a God whose marble bath
spilled. In a different beginning, before the pillars of civilization,
the city may have suggested a sane relief.
We have long feared openness
like a wounded person mystified by blood that speaks of a
sudden interior.
The way the brain *looks* woven suggests not going anywhere
like crumpled plans for a vast freeway of
whirling intersections
that just go around and around.

If gravity held onto the lovely a little stronger like need
all beauty could be made flat and less serious.
Citizens: facades.

Logic looks out a small
window at insanity and is able to breathe. Insanity is a rant of space
to a pilgrim of imagination who is exhausted.
The voice "can you represent me?" was a plot/
of land   animate prairie   its oral tradition bursting back.
How perfect to think that this city could only undulate here,
all madness
coughed up, built on the shoulders of gophers. The giant sloth was
the model.

The doctor wondered if I would reproduce the
asylum in my voice that the roof there kept the idea of
omniscience out and this poem allows you in and I have
moved with a logic and an idea of a city admitting its madness
has specific walls/ imagine each has a different purpose and
the problem of religion is solved.

This city instead glides a river forever between rhythm and melody
looking simply for another mind unadorned by the
distractions of illusory value and how and
where in this city could I find the God of privacy?
Away from advertising augury.
That is the question to commence the best flaneurian agency.
If you put me in this city/ I would be a sore thumb monument/
There's Waldo in a straight jacket sent/ holding an intangible reality.
The city is mad by nature/ like my poem by a park/ the portmanteau
stranger in the docks/ waiting for a personal ark. But
for those of us deemed "mad" or "crazy" there seems
no complete escape.
There is a piss river of paranoia emerging from our bodies as

if to re-become fish in nervous sweat we retract, lost in puddles
on your street. We are biological in this city spine aquaducted
by a chemical sewer/ a thorn flower bleeding
Technicolor
like a dripping tap.
This poem is made fragmented so that you sense
the struggle of our voice
in an obsession   of making sense.

A Guide to Light Loses and Finds Its Intentions

a)
Through insanity I found a voice, a personal genesis:
it was the first of times/ it was the whence of time.
Innocent light paled now in memory, a phoenix of
industry answering in a personal gyre... As a voice
my mind will convert polluted smoke into speech.
An undulating Icarus with albatross wings dicing
the singular non-poetic licensed lingos not to be lost on the cross
    retaining elan.
  The blue energy that keeps exhausted willows weeping, tempest tips
      but to the sky I would add a lucid scream... as it falls in memory.

Shakespeare: "Light seeking light doth light of light beguile."

"The preconceived *glimmer* of enlightenment is bewildered when
innocence's bright light is lost in broad daylight's narrow insight."
    This is a reading of the generality we call *life*.
For us: "madness's light seeking the cause of the world burning,
eventually flares memory's heated rose thrown into a confusion of
fallen stars and reels of manna exposed in those caches of light."

So then did "dark seeking dark doth dark of dark beguile?" Yes,
"Darkness layered by sleepless nights tricks evil
into a falling sky, and is a bruise to find the subtle blue
and finding nothing but ink-immune black."
There is in Zeno's paradox a vision of light in space;
that to return to previous light uses up the light just made.
But if the whole world sunk in an apocalypse
you would name a star "anchor" to prevent implosion.

And so to mention a city of light is to know that neon
of the old antique store and old star light of new galaxy news
might intersect somewhere in our heads for each of our stories
would evoke this city of burning as a delusion but realer
than realism.
A delusion on fire from outer space just thick smoke, a nightmare
image of the universe/ flashlights of stars looking for better
     personification.

b)
As Doctor Earwinker alluded to,
there really was an unconscious part of this new facility:
it was a dome, low lying, without a building,
made of unbreakable glass (a necessary material
for our bleeding minds and keeping away sharp things)
though I did not know this right away.
It was based on the sky and what tunnels beneath it, I wondered.
This dome arcade is the first thing for the City of Light's emergence.
The place where we could construct ourselves in relation to
the world around us.
I fantasize that the City of Madness
would possess a modern escalator to link future pilgrims on the
outside of an ivory tower made from the purest moon rock as a gesture
of the inside out that has been my experience throughout this poem.

8. (From *Notebook*— later in time that the time this current poem
was written).
      In case you were wondering, my diagnosis was: a creative
mind repressed by human disconnection. But this merely begs the
question; what clear medical mental illness did I have? My position
was also a strange take on "I think, therefore I am," which was meant
to separate the thinker from existence. I tried to do this with much
of my early life. In a strange way, I thought complexly, convolutedly,

therefore I really was, I existed and resisted, not just another fish going with the flow. I think also, you could add psychosis and depression to the mix, and look back on the wall text I had read as also useful, as I felt most of those feelings at one point or another though I would make changes. I perhaps meant to be witty, but I was also diagnosed with obsessive-compulsive disorder, which some might think is obvious by this page, if not earlier in my entire project. I realized that I *caused* an unconscious through repression but this is all after the following moment which I will express in a poem with some narrative elements:

c)
As we stood outside on the field
Doctor Earwinker, standing near me, said I should scream something,
    perhaps my name…
as some Yawpish conceit just to remove the residual *cliché*
from my throat.
He had heard of the idea of our thoughts bleeding and thought
if I could symbolically step outside myself I could
   climb on top of this sky/dome….
It seems it is made as a personal small prairie sky just for me.
His idea sounded like a "which disease? hunt test" to me, but there was
a kind of strange act of faith to it; should I look down once upon it?
Of course, I was worried that the glass would shatter but he said that
I should recall that the old etymology of schizophrenia means "a
    splitting of mind"
and he was certain I didn't have this. He felt that I had no ego
boundaries and that I was
simply suffering from too many thoughts caused by
trying to internalize the prairie and an overactive mind. I
    constructed a vast seal
to protect me from the sensing of everything.

He called out what he thought was the best reading of a scream:
Remember? The scream that is asking *how?*—to
all things, acknowledging the differences of all things.
We imagine only we can speak but we are conceited.
They could answer how they are and not *why?*
which is a tyrannical voice's question.

The sound would reach like Whitman's arm into endless fingers.
But should I quote sound in some molecular music
or should I sculpt?
As my hands touched the glass, I felt like a sculptor, but the material
 did not give
and I was able to get my way to the top, and it was as if I were
"out of my mind"
so that I was a performance piece of "The Thinker"
except now I posed "The Riddle," a work I had now become.

Madness is an element of the universe, an idea we "resort to."
Madness is negative capability's decadence, evil's bogus
distraction place.
Madness is the scarecrow a superhero pities and forms
an identity around.
Madness is a fill-in-the-blank of someone's eyes.
True madness is one dogmatic voice trying to silence others' voices

Besides, it is a plurality, and this is what occurred inside of me.
And then I thought musingly: what if the voice of God was
my own yell, and
I simply *forgot my self-expression?* Which was almost my story,
had it not been for these others who stirred my wonder into another
    life, this search
through the wormholes of my own mind and the briar patch of burrs
that are the baggage of a suffering that converts waste into knowing.

And through the imagined city I heard a voice calling me—
that might be mine in the future. Was it only the wind?

I knew that it was expected that I would scream now
that I was atop this edifice,
however: (the following verbose titles
were needed to contextualize the lack of understanding
still intrinsic to this entire work):

Colin Needing an Option to Scream/ Yawp: How to Breathe
Poetically in the Imagination Just before the Upcoming Cry:
(First Segment in a Five-Part Moment). For a Vicarious Yawp
(or Not) Or: The Other Author Demonstrates Polyphony Once-
and-for-All in Time's Context: A Birth of the Reader Yawp
if We Get the Idea of the Scream as a Thought-Intimation,
and Arguably Stop Right before the Scream Happens (See
Pun Ending of Obvious Concrete Poem of Gyre Shape)
Colin Can Be Imagined to Have His Own Scream Inside the
Text's Imagined Continuity (if He Wants)—Colin More in the
"Text" as Omniscient Narration Arrives in Place of God. We
Hear Breathing in these Cloud Breath Stanzas Below (First
Counterpoint Is with Thought and Internalizing the Prairie
First by Air then Wind). Each Breath Contained a Progressive
Thought Movement Towards Next Sections beyond
Immediately Here.

1. Inhale: (The Following Mind/ Body-Link Reminding Breaths
Can Be Seen as a Variation on Sonar in Backwards Reading:
See Very Last Line of Whole Text when the End Can Be
Projected Back as a New General Awareness).
Directly Below: Cloud-Breaths Go from Sharply Specific and
Rhymed to Abstract and Able to Read Other "Shapes."

A balance on the invisible is what our obsessive conscience and its
thousand-and-one delusions rests on/ I felt an earned scream swell in
the churning butter of my guts, like alphabetti digestion
in accordance with the anti-heroic lava lamp of the heart, but
something came to me—memory and intimation made a perfect
inner ambiance for me to perceive, with clarity: The voices I
witnessed were almost like the exposure by a tell-all-escope as if of a
comic book boom that had broken into hieroglyphic then language
vectors (if dark matters give) but also the language microscope
rendered me a gradual detective who also looked at micro biology
from the chemical that produces sensations of hope. (This is all to
say I will be clearing my mind of the easy imagist poetic, the simple
trope).

2. Exhale:

 We the "mad" have been talking for a long time but now a subjective
semiotic has blown up— the comic bubbles have burst/ and a fine
loss of ordinary breath informs the awareness that if you tried to
represent what we were able to feel/ you would enter panic's realm
where your mind is pulled (like a teenager lynched by his own lanky-
ness in the scene of endless judgement by satirical masterminds
whose diagnoses perforate the youths) and fully stretched
accordingly. With our conversations of still life weeds on the table
of society we play fortune teller cards while also gambling with fate

which we take to be a logical monster of surprises/ only now has implication caught up with our talk/ the road runner revealed as a phoenix our somnambulism subsequently a legitimate walk there is a balance of vision that goes to the birds but flight is not escapist nor is flightiness.

3. Inhale:

But, inside me it wasn't always simply words, like axioms or even comic bubbles but near ineffable idea-states and atom bomb feelings with epic sweep through the skin's maps/ raising absurd micro-cosmic mountains. Yet, a breath atmosphere around a kicked stone in my sudden vision of earth also felt impermeable and so all was preserved: a gorgeous bubble of universe/ where an earthiness is hidden somewhere in it all/ despite the un-described country of alienation/ this atmosphere *is the idea of a new air being internalized and the following yawp you must know that its surprise rhizome breath is designed so that you can stop anywhere to breathe again but try to go as long as you can (it has begun!)/ with longer suggested breath spaces than when the text started the first night in hospital/ to symbolize distance conquered:(but can anyone save breath in a preserve reservoir of windy Lethe)?*
  —There was a sudden gust of wind: I opened wide to eat it—

4. Exhale: Implausible Final Yawp: Intimation of a Language of Experience Second Counterpoint Where Reader Can Imagine/ Use Sound: Colin Fully Perceives Sick Consciousness's Vista and the Beauty and Pain of Growth with a Generative Effect of Mental Magnification: A Counterpoint Cry of an Imagined Scream of Seeing so Much in Ultimate Triumph of the Yawp, Defined As: A Scream as Idea of Witness of Suffering without Surrender which Could Loosen the Mind Compression of What Follows Immediately from this Title Section. Colin Shows His Creative Side with a Poorly-Rhymed Rant that He Only Thinks Of: "Possible Brief Walls of Sound Phonetically Broken by (Thought)ful Pauses of Panorama" Are the Reader's,— but Another Concrete Poem Is Right under Your Nose: Yet, Does the Reader Want to Scream by a Sudden Inversion of Frustration of Form Making Dis-function of Coherence? (Then Comes a Spatial Gyre that Is Really Agoraphobia Pressing the Sky upon He Who Can Now Support Its Pressure)...?

Colin: ("<u>My Thoughts Drifted towards Roary</u>")

The residual mysterious "it" of our idea-sources became so powerful/ almost like a voice of visitation from out of all previously-known contexts/ causing visions of a trap door's exposure that could levitate a sculpture on accumulated polite coughs of sulphuric breath but are more like the unconscious as a universe/ not hung-up on actual string theory my one-liners are quips here slightly quarks exceeding the tenuousness of theory and entering the lucid dreamer-web of things constructed in near mysticism (and every lie aimed where it wishes it could go: an idealism for conspiracy like a metanarrative still forge-able in our time) *mysterious* is the perfect code word for the question: how can the world—so clear and so apparent—be so confusing? *Mist steering us* into black bile quagmires/ passed yellow stones in exhausted fields/ all the voices could become a near-impossible text where an illustration becomes dimension, and the star systems were like our future childrens' mouths expressing ideas like new critics (before paraphrase's diffusion that is like experience generalized) from their pure initials of speech/ and with confused questions about distance in vast outer space felt and expressed from the back of every classroom/ all growth in retained space alters objects in that space to the ever-expanding human, feeling questions as if with Pound's artist answer-seeking antennae: in hospital sick-wards, this institution gives us light of the distant window as impossible guidance of suicide's map/ but here we grow larger but with a wiser moderation we shrink away from the body language of arrogant superfluous gestures into deeper reverences/ a daily death mask that is calloused by grasp and not touch the mime's lily acne-blossom absorbs mania in stretched eyes too/ further outside, a single voice is all the pagan choir making a single rising note that will become a scream/ with a little counterpoint we could speak of humble origins for the hospital/ another code word: *hummmm bull,* rejects simple mantras/ but some words work with that meditative nexus and a base, a foundation/ madness seems sometimes pagan and yet is preyed on by a single voice of answer/ against these winds do not totter/ with the biology of classifying by a new Aristotle meeting a Platonic subjective dodo bird/ a slightly winged but pickled thing an anomaly with Aristotle's categorizations flooded with mists that shift like a school of fish—so is diagnosis' nature/ the idea of a voice as able to answer all/ that assumes harmony is extractable from dissonance is a spill of puzzle/ with the defecting voices showing that the beauty of difference gets funnelled into mere competition, this is why the conformist makes cowards of us all: but daringly, the imagined first voice was dissonant to the silence, however harmonious it was/ because once the silence was so pure that it was not a numb closure, not now as it is pressed by snow-clichés and lies into a palimpsest that would dream into itself the possibilities of emptiness/ silence was impossibly like nothingness's euphemism—the first harmony was dissonance against the silence,

silence which was a better harmony/ in impossible continuity with itself but as with the newborn's tragic cry the idea was apparent—that we were still in a kind of new beginning, like a child's first Christmas/ but with Pandora's boxes filled with thoughtful toys/ Pinocchios of immeasurable Keatsian joys pointing to truth's retreat no, what I had experienced felt like a kind of adolescence, a broken allegorical one after a puberty of mind's gawky bifurcations yet a newness cast on everything/ now the results of a puberty floods the mind and our hands reach up our id remains hellishly below/ in our skies we spot the super-ego and is it a plane, yet the lowest of the humour lives here but this improves the foundational pun codes above as low as guts but not visceral as silver intestines digesting essentialist grit?/ so unlike a simple musical note and I had avoided playing solo on the grand piano of death/ but an x-ray reveals an old typewriter inside it—what this illness once meant: a darkness with flashes of lucid precision making little snaps that add up/ the rapaciousness of all of this here in this half-imaginative bombast of projection is that the voices of us are all still forming/ rejecting a new sprinkle of misleading stars over a bricolage voice of being killed by experience/ we are not fools in any dimming inner light either with the objective correlative of vomiting/ like our confessions with laughter as a disease spread by itching heads/ our laughter is exotic (to us) and our tears are not like the acidic blood from the movie *Aliens* with them falling forever/ the range of Rilke is evoked: a happy thing falling and we infer a sad thing rising and an ambivalent thing sitting—this is the trajectory of the voices' gravity/ and yet ambivalence can become everything because you can't be precise about reaction sometimes/ a scream is the last buoyant thing before the world falls apart/ the death of silence when dissonance is absolute/ yet, we find the Broca's region: *It's a matter of touch: push a finger caressingly and you find a poem—if you feel nothing in your finger but habit, a degenerate prose will emerge/ push hard and you find a scream/ puncture and you "find" madness enclosed like an implosion/ melted conventional*

windows are like sails to institutions/ then appears a mental ant farm,
carrying away mania's elated signature on depressed-gravity's shatter-
text into soon to-be-broken tunnel vision illustrations/ opening onto
potentially wordless awe's expanse as you leave personal suffering/ but
the semiotics of "touch" are implicit in all of synesthesia's effects at once
(inside and out) which abstracts touch/ we need contact with us
gradually moving into rooms more distant from each other evoking
an expanding universe/ and so for orientation you point up and ask
as a child might what the possibly diffuse clouds that block heaven
"say": we answer that they are a slow bureaucracy dealing with
amorphousness/ avoiding voluptuousness as the wind eats away at
everything with such a suckle you think of milk, steamed, until it
rains clarity in your haiku/ but those mists, they have a purpose: to
soften revelation as they make a pointillism of perforation with
semiotically mad stop lights winking ubiquitously/ but do these
words fall, too heavy, by being verbose enough for you to feel a
scream pit itself in you so that you need to crash these words against
a conceptual wall and have them return perfectly sorted? Does sense
make it back from expectation in paranoia's watch? Or does the
weight of heavy words act as a form of gravity if one put this text flat
the floor built into a possible room that you are no longer in but is
completed in time? I felt this all inside of me and it would be felt by
anyone and as one reads of it madness might gather in you also/
hopefully it is or will be broken by a mercy at the end of the day/ by
sanity's angels that mercifully never appear, by the dreams of
enlightened pacifism, the "to be or not be" soliloquy translated with a
good attitude towards a life reduced then to a life-style: *I think then*
of what time did to that leaning barn and I imagine sonar to re-prop it
and to imagine the confirmation of the fall of civilization elsewhere
(beyond the fertile flat lands of prairie) with a kamikaze catharsis of
blankness/ and perhaps I could still feel ignorance's greedy walls
collapse and all the walls I had seen that make this poetry more a
monument this wall of sound wall of silence/ yet the silence margin of

prairie relates to stigma of a text around madness: am I just pushing
silence back, a frame-pushing pedlar? And yet I reach to the other mad
institutions even with just a polite knock it is a scream that has its
energies *return* to its places of origin and thus the wind could be felt/
as you feel this/ internalized, returning and re-turning like a tongue-
centred gyre on possible rewind/ holding now a thousand goodbyes
of friends and enemies in an exact and ideal distance like a vision by
Dante/ we find the delusions that were crueler like the spine of pearl
or the earth planet's swerving hurl/ where the cosmology poem I
wrote could now unfurl: it was a moment of epics but as I catch my
breath this occurred—by the mysteries of which I feel humble, this
lowness of the pun is the gravity needed for this real world: the pun
is a double-take discourse-starter of terms technical to transcend and
from there you could re-read the text as it moved increasingly in
complex formal concepts or words: I imagine my friends against the
wind as it comes in gusts and I imagine a magpie with a shiny nail as
if to pitch this paper-thin tent of intent: my name's depiction: I revel
in the created nature of language so translatable in metaphor yet,
would I be able to imagine calling out that I have made poetic ideas
into poetic diction?

(

These   earlier   dissonant   rhythms   prior   are enemies
to   ease so that   some realize the   difficulty in   being able   to
sing   poetically of madness/   superseded by this   scream's
experiential emergence and its vision   airy disappearance/ with
phenomenological materialization but made   of fleetingness's urgency
and   referenced objects accumulate   like the walls to   withstand
sonar fully /sonar that is like the unexpressed sadness of our world
where the very power of   madness-silence's taboo=sonar (a force
in our   world not always "admitted") but the poem above adds to
reality, one-time possible delusions made into resonant objects
and abstract revealings   represent   delusions/ the mind made my
body fused hyper-real by a scream of choice: an expressive scream
converted to ideas flashing like death's scythe and sonar suggests
reciprocity in gravity's risen realm now of Blakean sand that
could be slipping through the fingers but is not (in some
sense here): as we see with his friends
imagin'd we see our hero
also: (Colin)
(out)

5. Representing Illness so Clear as to Cure Our Perception: Next: An Image of Thought Occurring "You Cannot Show Thought" —Ludwig Wittgenstein (These Lines an Unconscious under the Dome Making Colin Out from the Ground) Madness Distant from Its Condition Leads to the Empowerment of the Irrational's Capacity: A Close-Up Moment/ That Allowed the Above/ Light Speed Verses Below/ Voices of Cloud Moving in Wind/ The Synapse Was Expanded by Metaphor's Extension, Converted into Language: An Image of Causal Thought that Brings Space into the Mind—And Sonar Is Finally "The Return of the Absence of What You Long for but Don't Have" The Italic Lines below Push through these Strata of Explanation in Reverse Reading: See Cloud Breath's First Inhale Title—Is the below the Mad Synapse in the Internalization of Prairie?

Like a new form of terrible beauty/ as if partially liberated from form, my skull actually felt unreal—
transparent—like the dome my feet touch and the sun strikes like enlightenment, congeals
synapses that were exactly timed to that light internal/ external— they were qualitatively equal/
stirring the platonic in the sky/ the synapse finds thunder and an albatrossian Hamlet-go seagull/
moves over a swirling brain with its seas of troubled mind, and mere misery loses its gravitational pull.

Notes

I owe much to the work of Jorge Luis Borges, Jacques Derrida, Friedrich Nietzsche, Ludwig Wittgenstein, as well as Jack Kerouac. Borges's imagination is one of my major inspirations, particularly the way he sanctifies strangeness in such an innovative way in his text *Dreamtigers*. In *Sonar*, I have also tried to juxtapose neat, contained, but highly suggestive prose and poetry that is somewhat haunting.

Besides these, I would have to quote the thousands of poems I have read that are either echoed or silently inspirational in the making of my long poem. I hope, as a result, I have produced a kind of problem text, one that is well-rendered in form and imaginative in expression. Though tempted to veer off into philosophy, I have worked to keep this text predominantly literary.

If there was one poem that was most inspirational and which my work reacts in some ways against, it would be Allen Ginsberg's *Howl*. In some ways, my poem acts as a monolith akin to Ginsberg's work and it is perhaps likely that without the influence of his poem, writers like me would hardly know where to begin.

Acknowledgements

I have been so incredibly fortunate in being able to encounter amazing people in my life, and their indulgence in listening to me has been a creative resource for which I am forever grateful. I would like to thank Heather Roscoe, Matthew Tapscott, Julia Ryckman, Chris Macalino, Marla Braga, Dana Landry, and Alex Orange who all had their part in getting the ideas in this book into fuller manifestation by being great friends. I would also like to thank my breakfast group, who converted me to a morning person, a previously incomprehensible notion. I would also like to thank the amazing literary and artistic community of Winnipeg, from the academics to the most subterranean poet, and of course the great people at the Speaking Crow. Thanks also to Professors Deborah Schnitzer, Neil Besner, and Kathleen Venema among others for their inspiration and counsel. Thanks to everyone at Turnstone Press. And to all of my friends and family who have all had their moments.